The Green Flash
and Other Low Sun Phenomena

by

D. J. K. O'Connell, S. J.

With Photographs (80 in Colour)

by

C. Treusch, S. J.

VATICAN OBSERVATORY

1958

North Holland Publishing Company, Amsterdam
Interscience Publishers Inc., New York

➡

Sunset Dec. 28, 1955 – taken with Zeiss E-objective, focal length 6 metres, aperture 40 cm. on Kodak-Ektachrome daylight 1/50 second, enlarged 4.4 × on Ektachrome B, processed at the Specola Vaticana. At left are the time intervals of the chronograph in seconds. All five photographs are exactly in the same focus. See other notes on pages 26, 116.

PLATE I 3

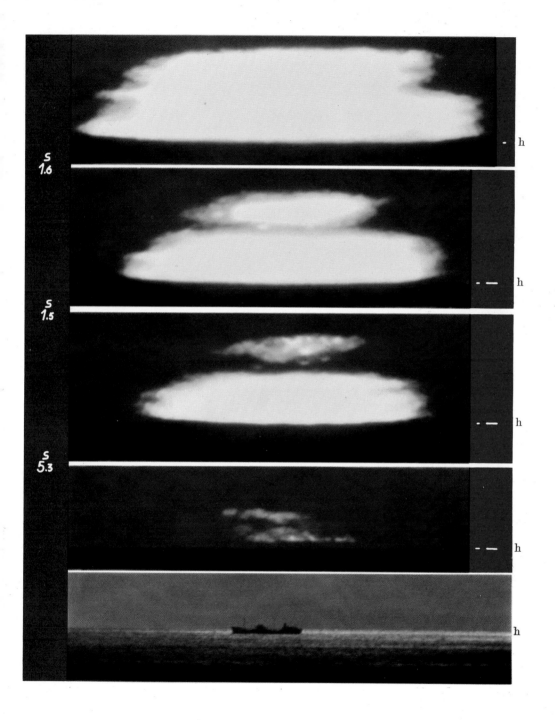

S
1.6

S
1.5

S
5.3

h

h

h

h

h

Contents

FRONTISPIECE (Plate I) 3

INDEX OF PHOTOGRAPHS 6

INTRODUCTION 7

I. HISTORY 7

II. THEORY OF THE GREEN FLASH 11

    1. Physiological Explanation 11
    2. Sea-wave Theory 12
    3. Anomalous Dispersion 12
    4. Atmospheric Dispersion 14
    5. Selective Absorption in the Atmosphere 15
    6. Rayleigh Scattering 17
    7. Absorption and Scattering due to Dust and Haze . . . 17
    8. Main Factors Causing the Green Flash 17

III. FACTORS THAT INFLUENCE THE GREEN FLASH 18

    1. Capriciousness of the Flash 18
    2. Duration of the Flash 18
    3. Varying Intensity of the Flash. Mirage Effects 19
    4. Increased Width of Green Rim. Abnormal Refraction . 20
    5. Scintillation 21
    6. Distortions of the Sun's Disc near the Horizon 22
    7. Colour of the Flash 23

IV. THE VATICAN OBSERVATORY PHOTOGRAPHS 24

    1. Introduction 24
    2. Telescopes 25
    3. Film and Development 25
    4. Exposure Times 26
    5. Effects of Over- and Under-Exposure 27
    6. Making Colour Movies of Scintillation on the Sun's Rim
       during Sunset 29
    7. Flashes Produced Artificially 29
    8. Reproduction Technique 30
    9. Arrangement of Photographs 31

ACKNOWLEDGEMENTS 32

PART A, THE GREEN RIM (*Colour Plates II-X and 7 black-and-white*
    plates) 34-70
    Average Vertical Extension of the Green Rim at Sunrise and
       Sunset 34
    Changes in the Green Rim 35

PART B. THE GREEN SEGMENT WITH GREEN FLASH (*Colour Plates*
    XI-XIV and 6 black-and-white plates) 71-100
    Sun's Zenith Distance at Sunsets over the Sea 99

PART C. THE GREEN AND THE RED FLASH INFLUENCED BY LAY-
    ERS OF DISCONTINUITY (*Colour Plates XV-XXI, 11 black-
    and-white plates*) 101-144

APPENDIX (*Colour Plates XXII-XXIV, 20 black-and-white plates*) 145-180
BIBLIOGRAPHY 181
SUBJECT INDEX 191
NAME INDEX 192

Index of Photographs

	Reproduced in Colour	*Black-and-White*
THE GREEN RIM	43, 77, 79, 119-29	
THE RED RIM	53, 119-29	
SUNRISE	41-51	37, 39
with Green Flashes	41, 47, 49, 51	57
Diffraction Effects		55
"Ray" Effects		57
SUNSET		
with Distortions of the Low Sun	119-29, 143	105, 107, 109-15, 156, 175
Green Segment Sequences	73, 77, 79, 119-29	
Green or Blue Flashes on the Horizon	3, 53, 73, 75, 77, 79, 129, 168	93, 95, 109-15, 133-5, 175
Green "Detached Strips"	3, 127, 129, 143, 168	57, 87, 93, 105, 111, 115, 161-3
"Blind Strips"		109-15, 137-41
Red Flashes	119, 121, 143	105, 107, 109, 175
Red Rim on the Green Segment	77, 79	
Lower Rim in Contact with Distant Sea Horizon	123	89, 91, 105, 107, 109-15, 135, 137, 139
Influence of Discontinuity Layers	119-29, 143, 168	85-93, 105, 107, 109-15, 133-5, 137-9, 156, 158, 161-3
THE SETTING MOON	65	
SETTING PLANET	67, 69	
INFLUENCE OF SCINTILLATION:		
Last Segment of Sun on Horizon	53, 77, 168	59, 91, 93, 95
Upper Rim	43, 77, 168	87, 93, 167
Lower Rim		61, 85, 89
Detached Green Strips	143, 168	87, 93, 161-3, 167, 171.
within Layers of Discontinuity		87-93, 161-3
Green Spikes	43	61, 87, 93
EXPERIMENTS WITH ARTIFICIAL LAYERS OF DISCONTINUITY	165	153-7
Comparison with Actual Layers of Discontinuity		156
EXPERIMENTS WITH ARTIFICIAL SUNSETS	165	159-60
Comparisons with Actual Sunsets		161
VARIOUS COLOUR EFFECTS CAUSED BY DIFFERENT EXPOSURE TIMES	173	
TECHNICAL EQUIPMENT		147, 148, 150, 153

Introduction

The phenomenon seen sometimes at sunrise or sunset, known in French as '*le rayon vert*' and in German as '*der grüne Strahl*', has sometimes been called in English by the corresponding term the '*green ray*', but it is usually known as the '*green flash*'. I shall use the latter designation in this paper, both as being common usage and as conveying a better idea of what is often seen than the word 'ray', which would lead one to expect a beam of light shooting up from the sun. Some sort of 'ray' of the kind has been reported, but very rarely indeed and only as seen with the naked eye. Some of the photographs reproduced here show how such an appearance can be simulated, even though there is no real 'ray', and it is likely that the reports of a 'green ray' can be explained in this way (cf pp. 57, 174-175).

Much attention has been devoted to the subject over the past seventy years or so, by astronomers, meteorologists and others. It pertains rather to meteorological optics than to astronomy proper; nevertheless a large proportion of the literature dealing with it has appeared in astronomical periodicals. In any case, the fact that the observational material presented in this paper could have been obtained only with astronomical equipment is sufficient reason for its appearance in an astronomical publication.

The aim of this paper is to reproduce photographs, both in colour and black and white, of the green flash and of kindred phenomena at the rising and setting of the sun (also of the moon and Venus) and of certain experiments carried out at the Vatican Observatory. All the photographs were taken by C. TREUSCH, S. J. Relevant meteorological and other data are given when available. References in the text and notes are to the bibliography at the end of the paper.

I. History

Although the main purpose of this work is to provide observational material rather than to discuss the various phenomena exhaustively, it seems well to begin by summarising previous researches in this field. I shall not attempt, however, to give a complete history of the subject, but only to provide sufficient background as a setting for the work done here.

The green flash appears at times so vivid, even to the naked eye, that it is surprising that the earliest explicit references to it are of comparatively recent date. One would expect that such diligent observers as the early astronomers of Babylonia, Chaldea and Egypt would have noted the phenomenon. In the clear skies of Egypt, for instance, it can be frequently seen, as has been noted by GROFF,[40, 41] OFFORD,[98] PIOT Bey,[106] PETRIE[104] and others. GROFF and PETRIE state that it is more brilliant at sunrise in Egypt, as the sky is then less red than at sunset. Archaeological evidence does indeed suggest that the green flash was familiar to the Egyptians very early in their history. This discovery is due to GROFF,[40] who points out that there are many references in ancient Egyptian writings to the green colour of the rising sun.*

Allusions to the green flash may be found in Celtic folklore. In the Isle of Man there are many traditional stories about the " *soillse bheó* " (*living light*), a mysterious emanation from the sun which, when it falls on certain herbs, confers on them almost miraculous healing powers. Miss C. M. BOTLEY [10] believes that this almost certainly refers to the green flash. Such stories probably go back to prehistoric times.

One would expect that such an indefatigable and careful solar observer as C. SCHEINER would have seen the green flash. In his huge tome, " *Rosa Ursina* ",[127] the larger part of which is devoted to his descriptions and drawings of sunspots, he does indeed mention various colours in the sun (p. 613) " de quibus in obseruationibus monui ". One who had the time to search through the hundreds of pages of observations might perhaps find a mention of the green flash. He refers more explicitly to colours he had observed in sunspots (p. 616) " Nimbi luminosi Maculis maioribus circumfusi, et colores extraordinarii, flaui, *subrufi, subuirides,*

---

* The sun during its nocturnal voyage was termed Mafkait, which is the name of an emerald-coloured mineral, so that the sun was considered to be green from sunset to sunrise. The sun's rays at sunset and sunrise are also sometimes called Tahen, a blue metal, which was also used to denote the blue colour of the sky. Night was the emblem of death, and Osiris, the god of the dead, was identified with the nocturnal sun. On the monuments Osiris is painted green when he is represented as the god of the dead. GROFF found a *stele* of the 5th dynasty on which the rising, or setting, sun is represented by a semi-circle coloured blue above and green below. He considers that this is the oldest known record of an astronomical observation.

necnon *caerulei* adhaerentes, prout etiam alii in Germania obser-
uarunt et notarunt, quemadmodum in lib. 3 satis dictum et doc-
tum ". Book 3 is the very long one containing the observations,
and I have not found time to read through it. It does seem likely,
however, that SCHEINER observed the red and green (or blue)
rims of sunspots, due to atmospheric dispersion when the sun is
low. He certainly observed sunrise and sunset for several years,
both at Ingolstadt and at Rome, and wrote a book on the distortions of the sun when near the horizon, with many interesting
descriptions and drawings,[128] but I have not found any mention
of the green flash in this work.

It has been suggested[1] that NEWTON mentions the green flash,
but that he thought it purely subjective. I have not been able
to discover where this appears in NEWTON'S writings.

Archaeologists and historians of science, once their attention
has been called to the matter, may find other early indications
of observations of the green flash. Care must be taken, however,
to distinguish it from the green, or blue, sun or moon, a rare
occurrence totally different in origin to the green flash. A green
or blue sun was frequently seen after the great Krakatoa eruption
of 1883[121] and attracted much attention. Similar phenomena[159]
were observed more recently, due to great forest fires in Alberta,
Canada, on September 23, 1950. I have found references to the
'green flash' or 'green ray', where the descriptions showed clearly
that the observations were of the green sun.

Perhaps the trained eye of some artist may have noticed the
green flash. In this connection one thinks of such superb landscape
artists as CLAUDE and COROT, both of whom were particularly
interested in sunrise and sunset phenomena, but, so far as I am
aware, neither gave any hint that he had observed the green
flash.

Early Observations. In 1815 S. LEE,[79] Secretary of the Royal
Society, published a study of atmospheric refraction and dispersion. He records observations of Mars near the horizon and
notes that the upper rim was blue and the lower rim red. The
effects of atmospheric dispersion on star images near the horizon
were of course familiar to BESSEL and others who investigated
astronomical refraction. AIRY[4] even invented an eyepiece to
counteract atmospheric dispersion, with a view to improving
observations of the transit of Venus when the sun was low.

The earliest observation of the green flash of which I have

been able to find a record was made by W. SWAN[135] on September 13, 1865. From the Righi he saw a dazzling emerald green flash at sunrise over a distant mountain. His account was not published until 1883. The earliest published reference is to a letter written by J. P. JOULE to the Manchester Literary and Philosophical Society in 1869, recounting his observations of the green flash. JOULE refers to observations made by BAXENDELL, but these observations were, it seems, communicated privately to JOULE and not published. JOULE's letter itself does not seem to have been published, but extracts from it are given in a paper by D. WINSTANLEY,[160, 161] who describes the green flash from his own observations: " The green ray ... begins at the points or cusps of the visible segment of the sun, and when the setting is nearly complete, extends from both cusps to the central space between, where it produces the momentary and intense spark of coloured light visible to the unaided eye ". This is an excellent description of what we often see here. WINSTANLEY notes that the last flash is sometimes bluish-green and sometimes, as seen also by JOULE, quite blue.

W. J. FISHER[34] suggests that Jules VERNE's romance " *Le Rayon Vert* " (1882)[145] first attracted general attention to the green flash. This may very well be. It is certainly striking that I have not found any references prior to 1882 apart from those already mentioned. Various early accounts of the green flash, such as that by Lord KELVIN, refer explicitly to VERNE's novel. KELVIN[69] saw a blue flash in 1899 just before the sun rose over Mont Blanc. He had previously observed the green flash at sunset (about 1893).[69, 70]

In the past seventy years or so a great deal has been written on the green flash, not all of equal value. The first comprehensive discussion is that by W. J. FISHER,[34] who also describes very many observations made by himself and others. In the following year, 1922, appeared a book on the green flash by M. E. MULDER,[94] who gives a digest of previous literature and discusses the cause of the phenomenon. P. F. KUIPER[75] in his Utrecht doctoral thesis (1926) gives details of many hundreds of observations, made mainly on Dutch ships due to the initiative of A. A. NIJLAND. KUIPER gives a thorough discussion of the phenomenon and of its possible causes. More recent discussions of value, in order of appearance, have been published by S. W. VISSER,[146] Chr. JENSEN,[62] R. G. AITKEN,[5] R. MEYER,[89] T. S. JACOBSEN.[57]

II. Theory of the Green Flash

1. *Physiological Explanation.* Many who have seen the green flash held that it is purely physiological in origin, fatigue of the retina causing the complementary colour to be seen after the eye had been dazzled by the reddish rays of the setting sun. Observations of the flash at sunrise were, of course, in themselves sufficient to prove that the phenomenon is not purely subjective. As already mentioned, the earliest observation of which I have found record was made at sunrise. It is rather odd that the observer himself, Professor SWAN,[135] commented "I do not doubt that the phenomenon was purely subjective, for before sunrise the sky was all lit up of a magnificent crimson hue ", for it is clear from his description (quoted above, p. 10) that what he had observed was a typical brilliant green flash. KELVIN's observation of a blue flash at sunrise attracted much attention at the time, owing to his great reputation. He certainly did not think that the colour was all in his eye. Yet these observations seem to have been soon forgotten or overlooked, for the subjective explanation continued to receive strong support, even from such an experienced astronomer as W. H. PICKERING.[105] Sir Oliver LODGE at first thought that it was subjective,[81] but changed his mind later on.[82] Professor PORTER[108] performed an experiment which, he held, proved that the green flash is purely subjective. He caused a bright red artificial sun to be occulted behind an artificial horizon and saw the complementary green colour after the " sun " had disappeared.

There have been many observations of the flash at sunrise, as well as at the rising of Venus and of bright stars. Further proof of the objectivity of the phenomenon was provided when DANJON and ROUGIER[23, 24, 25] photographed the spectrum of the green and red rim of the low sun (1920). Yet even in very recent years the subjective explanation has found vigorous supporters.[20] D. M. BARRINGER[8] saw a brilliant green flash and tried to photograph it simultaneously on colour film with an 8 mm motion-picture camera. Since he failed to record the flash on the film, he concluded that the cause was purely physiological, whereas there was no chance of photographing the flash with such a short focal length. One physician-astronomer[71] proposed a physiological explanation of another kind — he held that the green flash was a sign of biliousness!

2. *Sea-wave Theory*. Another curious theory of the green flash found several supporters, i.e. that it was caused by the dispersion of the sunlight passing through the crests of waves on the horizon. This theory was suggested in 1887.[99] It was revived many years later by C. D. PERRINE,[102] who, however, later on[103] admitted that the colour was due to atmospheric dispersion. The fact that the flash is also seen over a land horizon disposes completely of this theory. Some even held that the green colour was due to the passage of the light through the green sea water!

After reading such arguments, repeated ad nauseam, I sympathise with Sir Arthur SCHUSTER's outburst[133] "The same arguments are repeated over and over again, until we feel that a horse dead and duly flogged had better be buried; this might save us from being worried by its ghosts and reincarnations". He then suggests that it is time that the green flash should find its place in elementary text-books, " only by this means shall we be saved from further discussions covering the same ground ".

3. *Anomalous Dispersion*. W. H. JULIUS[64, 65] suggested in 1901 that the rarity and the variable duration of the greeen flash could be explained if it were due to anomalous dispersion in the earth's atmosphere, i.e., if, in the neighbourhood of some telluric line, or lines, in the sun's spectrum, the longer wave-lengths were refracted more than the shorter, thus producing a reversal of that part of the spectrum. He did not attempt an experimental verification of his theory, but suggested that someone should try to photograph the spectrum of the green flash, although he appreciated the difficulty of the task.

This theory of JULIUS attracted a good deal of attention. G. GUGLIELMO,[44] who had made many excellent observations of the green flash at sunrise and at sunset at Cagliari, Sardinia, tried various experiments to see whether anomalous dispersion played any part in producing the green rim and green flash. He found that the dispersion with a 10° prism was too great compared with that of the atmosphere. He found the same difficulty with a spectroscopic eyepiece. A diffraction grating in front of the objective gave too complicated a result. Finally he made a water prism giving about the same dispersion as the atmosphere. This prism he placed in front of the objective (f.l. 163 cm) with the refracting edge vertical, thus, together with the dispersion of the atmosphere, producing the effect of crossed prisms. Any appreciable anomalous dispersion should have produced a bending of the lines affected, but no such change was observed. He concluded that anomalous dispersion had no appreciable effect on the green flash.

Following a suggestion of GUGLIELMO'S, RUDA[122] tried to test the theory in another way. JULIUS had suggested that free ions high in the atmosphere produce absorption lines in the green region of the solar spectrum and that anomalous dispersion occurs near these lines, causing the green flash. Thus this part of the absorption spectrum of ionised air should differ from that of non-ionised air. RUDA used an interference method, passing one beam of sunlight through ordinary air, the other through air ionised by X rays. High dispersion was used and various air pressures. RUDA found no difference whatever between the index of refraction of ionised and of non-ionised air. He does not claim that the negative result of his experiments is a definite refutation of JULIUS' theory, but he does believe that it shows that anomalous dispersion does not play any appreciable part in the formation of the green flash.

DANJON and ROUGIER[23, 24, 25] also carried out experiments to test JULIUS' theory. In 1920 they photographed, for the first time, the spectrum of the green and red rim of the low sun from the tower of Strasbourg Cathedral. They used a spectrograph, with the slit horizontal. They found no trace of anomalous dispersion and concluded that normal atmospheric dispersion and absorption are adequate to account for the green rim and the green flash. RUDA does not seem to have known of this work of DANJON and ROUGIER, just as the latter apparently were not aware of GUGLIELMO's experiments.

Another, and very elaborate, series of experiments to test JULIUS' anomalous dispersion theory was carried out by G. A. TIKHOV.[140] In 1921 he started photographing the spectrum of the upper and lower rim of the low sun on the island of Kildine in the Arctic. In 1923 he began using the crossed prism method. He used a plane grating with the spectrograph slit vertical, giving a dispersion perpendicular to that of the atmosphere, the first order dispersion being 190 Å/mm. The experiments were made first at Pulkovo and then at Staroïé Garkolovo on the Gulf of Finland, both at sunrise and sunset, with exposures of from 0.4 to 32 seconds. Several spectra showed traces of anomalous dispersion beside lines A, B and a. TIKHOV continued the experiments with improved apparatus and obtained in all more than 2,000 spectrum photographs, including some of the green flash and many of green (and red) detached strips. He concludes that anomalous dispersion is produced in the earth's atmosphere. It is, however, extremely difficult to detect and it can hardly have an appreciable effect on the formation of the green flash. TIKHOV does not seem to have known of the researches of GUGLIELMO and RUDA.

TIKHOV mentions that he had already built a more powerful spectrograph with the object of continuing this work, but I have not been able to find any further publication by him on this subject. It is probable that the spectrograph itself was destroyed when the Pulkovo Observatory was wrecked during the war. It is strange that I have not come across any mention of this careful and important piece of research.

4. *Atmospheric Dispersion.* It is clear that atmospheric dispersion is at least a main factor in the formation of the green flash. Lord RAYLEIGH[112] carried out an interesting series of experiments to determine whether the normal dispersion of the atmosphere is large enough to explain the effect " or whether we must appeal to special conditions such as cause mirage ". He used a prism with the same dispersive power as the atmosphere, with either diffuse skylight or an opal bulb as the source, the spectrum being received on a screen. Using an artificial horizon he produced at will a red or blue flash (with diffuse skylight) or a blue-green flash (with the opal lamp). He does not seem to have known of earlier work on these lines. He considered that normal atmospheric dispersion is adequate to explain the green flash.

A few years later[113] RAYLEIGH carried out further experiments on artificial sunsets. He investigated particularly the contrast effects of a red or orange background, and concluded that they are not important in this connection.

A very interesting observation of an artificial green flash made many years earlier is worth mentioning. In 1910 Capt. G. COUTINHO[21] of the Portuguese Navy was engaged in a geodetic survey in Mozambique. When exchanging heliograph signals with another officer at a site about 80 metres higher and separated from him by 50 km of sea, he saw the green flash at the point where the light disappeared below the horizon. By moving his head up or down he found that it was visible over a vertical range of about 20 cm (this gives about 0″.8 for the width of the green flash, corresponding to a refraction of about 2′.3). He again saw a ' green flash ' at night at the same site when an acetylene lamp was used instead of the heliograph.

5. *Selective Absorption in the Atmosphere.* The green is cut off more or less abruptly on the side of greater wave-length by various telluric absorption lines and bands, which absorb most of the orange and yellow. Conspicuous among these are BREWSTER's bands,* due to water vapour. In addition there are lines or bands due to oxygen and ozone, as well as the Janssen bands, due apparently to O_4. In 1885 J. JANSSEN,[59] in the course of his laboratory experiments at Meudon Observatory, discovered in the visual region of the oxygen spectrum some sharp, hitherto unknown, absorption bands, which are known by his name. He calculated that the strongest of these bands, at 577 mμ, should be visible in the solar spectrum, but he failed to detect it at Meudon, where it was masked by a neighbouring rain-band. Later on he went to the Sahara and there observed the spectrum of the low sun. In the very dry air the rain-bands were much weaker and JANSSEN observed, or believed that he observed, the 577 mμ band.[60]

The discovery of the Janssen bands seems to have remained without consequence until recent years, when it has been followed up actively. KEILIN and HARTREE,[66, 67] who give references to other work on the subject, conclude that these bands are due to O_4. T. S. JACOBSEN[56] claims to have detected the Janssen bands in his very interesting study of photographs of the spectrum of the low sun and of the green flash. These photographs were taken in the Hawaiian Islands at sea level on colour film, with a diffraction grating in front of a short focus lens. The films were not calibrated and I think that, especially in view of DUFAY's work, further evidence is required before this identification can be accepted.

J. DUFAY[29] has made a careful study of atmospheric absorption. He notes that it is practically impossible to disentangle

* BREWSTER[11] was the pioneer observer in this field, but it was JANSSEN who coined the name " raies telluriques "[58]. The water vapour bands are often called ' rain-bands', since it was believed at one time that an increase in their strength portended rain. KUIPER, in his discussion of the observations made by E. HAVINGA and other Dutch seamen, showed that the green flash is more likely to be seen when the atmospheric humidity is high (ref. 75, pp. 45-49).

the strongest Janssen band, at 577 mμ, from the bands due to water vapour, oxygen and ozone. Referring to JANSSEN's observations of this band DUFAY comments " Les observations visuelles de JANSSEN paraissent, dans ce cas, sans valeur ". As stated above, the existence of the Janssen bands due to O_4 is well established by laboratory experiments, but their behaviour in the atmosphere still remains to be investigated. In particular it is quite unknown whether they vary in intensity, apart from the effect of increasing air-mass.

The most recent discussion of selective absorption in the atmosphere is that by GOLDBERG.[39] He notes that the O_4 bands at 577 mμ and 629 mμ, " although probably present are blended with stronger bands of O_2 ", in agreement with DUFAY's conclusion (cf. also GOLDBERG's Table 4, p. 547).

There is perhaps a hint of another factor which may influence the green flash in a suggestion made by MÜLLER and KRON[95] (in quite another connection). They went in 1910 to the island of Teneriffe where they made a long series of measurements of atmospheric extinction for various wave lengths at different heights above sea level. They noticed that the curves showing the decrease of the transmission coefficient of the air with decreasing λ had a still-stand in the green region of the solar spectrum from about 570 mμ to 540 mμ, indicating that the rate of decrease of transparency was appreciably less in this region than elsewhere in the visible spectrum. This fact had been noted also by SCHUSTER,[132] at about the same time, in C. G. ABBOTT's long series of measures of atmospheric transmission. The effect appears in every series of measures made at altitudes from sea level to over 3,000 metres. MÜLLER and KRON believe that water vapour is not responsible, for the amount of water vapour in the atmosphere above the highest station (Alta Vista) was extremely small. They conclude " Vielleicht spielt das Ozon oder irgend ein anderes permanentes Gas in der Atmosphäre eine bisher noch unbekannte Rolle ". They suggest that further research on this point would be of interest. If such researches have been made, I have not seen any references to them and I can only repeat MÜLLER and KRON's recommendation that they would be worth while.

It is curious, by the way, that these authors do not mention having seen the green flash, although they observed from sunrise to sunset for about a month, under what would seem to be ideal conditions.

6. *Rayleigh Scattering.* The intensity of the light of shorter wave lengths is diminished by scattering by air molecules, the scattering varying as λ^{-4}, as was shown many years ago by RAYLEIGH. The effect decreases with increasing height above sea level and depends also on the meteorological conditions. In general, one may say that an observer at sea level, under normal atmospheric conditions, will not receive, from the low sun, light of wave length shorter than the green. An observer at higher altitudes, and even at lower levels if the air is unusually clear, may receive blue light, and even very rarely violet light, from the low sun.

7. *Absorption and Scattering due to Dust and Haze in the Atmosphere.* Dust and haze can produce a general absorption of sunlight, more or less independent of wave length, as well as selective absorption or scattering depending on wave length. The effect on light from the low sun varies very greatly, depending both on the size and the number of particles in the light path.

8. *Main Factors Causing the Green Flash.* To sum up, one may safely assert that the chief factors involved in the formation of the green flash are atmospheric dispersion, selective absorption in the atmosphere and the scattering and absorption mentioned in (6) and (7) above. When at sunset the upper rim of the sun is nearly touching the horizon, most of the orange and yellow light is absorbed by the atmosphere and the light of longer wave length has already set below the horizon. If, in addition, the blue and violet are scattered, there is left a narrow green rim. Owing to the absorption of the orange and yellow, the transition to green is abrupt, not gradual as it would be in the absence of selective absorption. With normal atmospheric dispersion the width of the green rim is of the order of 10″, but it may be two or three times as great (for observations made here see pp. 34, 35), if the refraction and dispersion are greater than normal and if other influences are present, such as reflection in inversion layers or scintillation. Some of these factors may have the effect not only of increasing the width of the green rim, but also of increasing the intensity of the green light. Under such conditions one may perceive a brilliant green flash at the moment of sunset. The green flash may even appear completely detached from the sun's disc and floating above the horizon when the sun has disappeared, as may be seen in some of the photographs in this paper.

These other factors which may affect the duration or intensity of the flash will be considered in Part III.

III. Factors that Influence the Green Flash

1. *Capriciousness of the Flash.* It often happens that the flash is not seen under conditions which appear to be similar to those under which it had been seen easily. Thus AITKEN notes[5] that at some periods he saw it regularly from Lick Observatory, whereas sometimes he failed to see it for months on end. It must be borne in mind that the great majority of observations of the flash have been made with the naked eye. For a mean horizontal refraction of 35' the width of the green rim at sunset due to atmospheric dispersion is about 10''. A perfect human eye could in theory resolve two points of light 25'' apart. HELMHOLTZ found that in practice a separation of at least 1' is required, and in most cases the limit is probably nearer 2'. Thus the naked eye cannot distinguish the green rim until it alone remains above the horizon, and even then it cannot distinguish any details, although they may be easily visible in a telescope. Various photographs reproduced here show very fine details indeed, and often show a mixture of colours which are distinguishable only with high magnification. Factors which facilitate the seeing of the green flash are increased duration and intensity, and increase in width of the green rim.

2. *Duration of the Flash.* The duration depends on the rate at which the sun is rising or setting. WHITMELL[158] calculated that at certain times near the Arctic circle the green flash may last for 12 minutes. GUGLIELMO[45] made a careful study of the theoretical duration of the flash and found that near Hammerfest (79° N) it might last for 14 minutes (i.e. 7 minutes at sunset + another 7 minutes when sunrise follows immediately on sunset). A further increase is obtained when the sun at rising or setting follows the slope of a mountain. MINNAERT[91] and others have been able to keep the green flash in view by moving along a slope at the right speed. The longest duration on record is that reported by BYRD's Antarctic expedition[47] at Little America (78° S) in 1929, when the sun grazed the irregular horizon of the barrier ice and the green flash was seen on and off for about 35 minutes. There was a strong temperature inversion near the ice surface at the time, which no doubt intensified the flash. The refraction was probably abnormal, causing the sun to remain longer above the horizon than usual. The observer, W. C. HAINES, looked for the

green flash in vain many times under what seemed similar conditions (but when there was probably no temperature inversion).

An interesting observation made here by C. TREUSCH is worth recording. He was watching sunrise over Rocca Priora with the finder (f.l. 1 m) of the visual refractor and a neutral filter. At the edge of a cloud (2° above the horizon), moving upwards with the sun, he saw a very bright green flash for 30 seconds on end. The cloud had a very sharp edge. The flash was quite broad, not a point, and its brightness was constantly varying.

3. *Varying Intensity of the Flash. Mirage Effects.* The Little America observation, mentioned above, shows the influence of a temperature inversion. EVERSHED[31, 32, 33] suggested long ago that the abnormal conditions that produce mirage effects have an influence on the green flash. He noted that every evening on shipboard between NW Australia and Java a brilliant green flash was seen, and at the same time a mirage effect was conspicuous, due to a thin layer of low density in contact with the sea. " At sunset the last segment of the disappearing limb was ... reflected and reversed, causing a lenticular shape with the cusps raised about 1′ above the horizon. The green flash occurred when the green-edged cusps coalesced into a single bright patch ". He then mentions his well-known observation of the setting of Venus, when a reflected image of the planet appeared moving upwards to meet the descending image, and the instantaneous and conspicuous change of colour from dull red to green took place at the moment of meeting of the two images. " It seems to me evident from these observations that the mirage layer greatly intensifies the ordinary dispersion effect, by adding the light from the reflected image to the direct image at the moment of setting ". R. W. WOOD[162] reported similar observations some years later.

An increase in intensity of the light when a bright green flash is seen visually has indeed been observed frequently enough, but the first experimental confirmation was given by T. S. JACOBSEN[56] in his study of the spectrum photographs of the green flash, already referred to. His measures of the relative intensities of the spectra of the low sun and of the green flash led him to conclude that " the composition of the sunlight reaching the observer during a green flash is definitely so changed as to throw more intensity into the green and blue-green regions of the spectrum... The flash was thus a real brightening of green light just preceding sunset... Whenever an intensification is observed, it seems reasonable to assume that a mirage condition or a reflection from an inversion layer must enter into the explanation of the phenomenon ". Our experience here fully accords with these conclusions.

4. *Increased Width of Green Rim. Abnormal Refraction.* GUGLIELMO, in his long series of observations of the green flash at sunrise and sunset, found that the green rim was sometimes two or three times its theoretical width.[44] Our observations confirm this (cf. pp. 34, 35). When the refraction is greater than normal, the dispersion and the width of the green rim are also increased.

Commenting on R. W. WOOD's suggestion[162] that exceptionally large dispersion near the horizon may make the flash more easily visible, Lord RAYLEIGH[112] writes " if the variations are of much importance in this connection, we must suppose the refraction on some occasions to be at least double the ordinary. This would defer the time of sunset by two minutes or more ". He suggests that the actual time of sunset be compared with the predicted time, and that the green flash be looked for simultaneously. "I am hoping", he adds, "to get observations in tropical seas through the good offices of the Astronomer Royal ". I do not know if this suggestion was followed up. In any case, equivalent observations have been made by VISSER and VERSTELLE,[148] who often observed the green flash at sea and at the same time measured the dip of the horizon. The mean value of the sun's zenith distance observed here for thirty sunsets with green flash is 91° 33.'3, and for eleven sunsets when no flash was seen 91° 31.'3 (cf. p. 99). This difference suggests that the refraction is somewhat greater when a flash is seen, although no close correlation was found between the sun's zenith distance (or the refraction) and the occurrence or duration or intensity of a green flash. The absence of any marked correlation is not surprising, for many other factors may be at work, particularly reflections (in inversion layers) and scintillation, and it is hardly possible to disentangle the various influences. The maximum zenith distance observed here is 91° 41.'5. The horizontal refraction was then about 44' (cf. p. 100), only 9' more than the normal value. This increase is not sufficient to have a noticeable effect on the green flash. It by no means follows that variations in refraction may not play an important part in the production of the green flash in other localities, e. g. in the Arctic regions.

Many remarkable instances of abnormal refraction are on

record (cf. PERNTER-EXNER,[101] pp. 84-91). Corsica has often
been seen from the Riviera.[77, 187] TIKHOV[140] measured refractions
of over 2° at Pulkovo. The most striking case is that reported
by Dutch mariners at Novaya Zemlya in 1597, when they saw
the sun for 14 days, when it should have been below the horizon,
the refraction reaching more than 4°. The report was studied by
KEPLER and others, and many concluded that the observation
was impossible. Some held that there must have been some confusion in the dates, owing to the recent reform of the calendar.
It is certain that there was no mistake in the dates and that the
observations were correct. The latest and most thorough discussion is that by S. W. VISSER,[147] who points out that a similar
observation was made in the Weddell Sea in 1915 by Sir Ernest
SHACKLETON during his last Antarctic expedition.

   5. *Scintillation* can have a marked influence on the green rim
and the green flash. Strong scintillation causes an appreciable
broadening of the rim, but at the same time a lessening of the
intensity of the colour, so that the effect on a (visual) observation
is hardly predictable. Some of the photographs reproduced here
show interesting scintillation effects, although it has proved impossible to reproduce some of the extremely fine (and rapidly changing) details, even with very high magnification.

   One point emerges very clearly from our observations — the
rim of the low sun can be very strongly disturbed by scintillation
even when the very distant horizon is extremely clear and sharply
defined, showing that the cause of the scintillation is not always
in the lower layers of the atmosphere. This accords fully with
WEGENER's conclusion (ref. 150, p. 206) " ... dass die untersten
Luftschichten, in welchen man nach meteorologischen Erfah-
rungen am ehesten solche eng gedrängten Störungen des Bre-
chungsquotienten erwarten würde, offenbar für die Erklärung der
Szintillation nicht in Betracht kommen. Der Sitz derselben dürfte
vielmehr hauptsächlich in den hohen und höchsten Schichten
der Atmosphäre zu suchen sein ".

   Many years ago GALLISOT and BELLEMIN[37] announced the
discovery of a disturbed layer (couche troublée) in the atmosphere, the height of which seemed to have a remarkable relation
with the weather. They found the height of the layer to vary
between 2,300 and 5,000 m. They attribute the production of
shadow-bands to undulations in this layer. J. DEVAUX[27] thought
that the green strips that he had observed detached from Venus

when the planet was near the horizon might be due to the same cause.

Since then, of course, a great deal of research has been carried out on scintillation and ' seeing ', particularly in very recent years, e.g. at the Dunsink, Edinburgh and U. S. Naval Observatories. Important theoretical studies have been made by GAVIOLA,[38] CHANDRASEKHAR,[15] KELLER[68] and others (the last two papers contain many references to earlier literature). CHANDRASEKHAR holds, with RAYLEIGH and others, that scintillation at small zenith distances is to be attributed to another cause than the phenomena observed near the horizon, and that at high altitudes above the horizon " we must attribute ' seeing ' and scintillation to the corrugation of an incident plane wave-front by its passage through a ' disturbed region ' in the atmosphere ". The disturbed layer (probably an inversion layer) is presumably in a state of turbulence. CHANDRASEKHAR estimates the thickness of this turbulent layer as of the order of 100 metres and its height as of the order of 3 or 4 km. (WEGENER considered that the layers responsible for scintillation are only a few centimetres, at any rate less than 1 metre, thick).

While it is true, of course, that disturbances in the lower layers of the atmosphere can, and often do, have marked effects on the images of stars near the horizon, nevertheless our observations prove, I think conclusively, that strong scintillation can be observed near the horizon which in no way depends on the conditions in the lower atmosphere.

6. *Distortions of the Sun's Disc near the Horizon.** Some observers[196] have noted that certain forms of distortion of the sun's disc are likely to be followed by a green flash. The earliest published observations of these distortions are those by C. SCHEINER,[128] some of whose drawings are reproduced here (Appendix, p. 180).

* Dr. BAER,[6] a careful observer who had noted the distortions of the sun's disc at both sunrise and sunset and published very good drawings of them, was afraid that unkind people might be suspicious about the cause of the distortions and thought it well to state solemnly " Um gleich dem Einwande zu begegnen, dass meinerseits eine physische oder optische Täuschung bei diesen Beobachtungen vorliegen könne, bemerke ich, dass ich Temperenzler bin, also alkoholischen oder sonstigen narkotischen Einflüssen nicht unterstehe, und dass ich zwei gesunde, emmetropische (normalsichtige) Augen mit etwa 5/3, also übernormaler Sehschärfe besitze. Ich kann demnach mit bestem Gewissen die Wahrheit der hier mitgeteilten Tatsachen bekräftigen ".

Other interesting drawings were published by ARCTOWSKI,[2, 3] RICCÒ,[117] KRIFKA,[73] and photographs (black and white) by COLTON,[17, 18, 19] RUDAUX,[124, 141] and CHAPPEL.[16] Mirage effects were studied by TAIT[136, 137] and others (references in PERNTER-EXNER,[101] pp. 84-188). WEGENER[150] investigated the influence of layers of discontinuity on the appearance of objects near the horizon (pp. 212-225). In particular he calculated the forms the sun's disc should assume owing to the presence of inversion layers; the term ' blind strip ' is due to him. Several of our photographs illustrate WEGENER's calculated deformations of the sun's disc.

7. *Colour of the Flash.* At high altitudes and with very clear air, when the Rayleigh scattering is less, the colour of the flash is more likely to be blue or blue-green. Many observations of a blue flash are on record. BARNARD[156] suggested long ago that it be called the ' Blue Flash ', for he usually saw it blue from Lick Observatory. JACOBSEN[56] reports the same for the SW Pacific. HERTZSPRUNG, who has often observed the flash, also considers that it is likely to be blue when the air is clear (private communication). Our experience here confirms this.

GINDRE[215] has a very interesting account of the change in colour of the flash when, from Lyons Observatory, he observed the sun rise over the Alps. Ten minutes before sunrise a green fringe appeared along the crest of the mountains, evidently caused by a green flash at sunrise over the plains of Lombardy lighting up the powdered snow, stirred up by a strong wind. A blue flash (about 470 mμ) was seen at sunrise, lasting about 0.5 sec.; after 2 seconds he estimated the wave length of the light he saw as 530 mμ, after another 4 seconds as 570 mμ, turning to orange after 2 seconds. The sun was moving parallel to the mountain slope, thus causing the increased duration.

Very occasionally a *violet flash* has been seen. No pure violet flash has been seen here so far, although a blue flash has been seen often and sometimes a blue verging towards violet.

A *red flash* below the sun has been noted by a very few observers, e.g. when the lower limb of the sun emerges from below a cloud. It has been photographed here a number of times.

Sunspots when near the horizon have a red rim above and a green rim beneath, as one would expect, since the upper border of a spot is the lower border of a more luminous area. Red or green strips, detached from the borders of the spots, have sometimes been observed here. They are very difficult to photograph.

IV. The Vatican Observatory Photographs

1. *Introduction.* In 1933, while I was staying at the Lick Observatory, I looked regularly for the green flash, together with the Director, Dr. R. G. AITKEN, who had often seen it there. Our efforts were unsuccessful, as were the many attempts that I made in other places, until I saw it for the first time, and very clearly, at sunset over the Mediterranean from my office window at Castel Gandolfo. Some of our telescopes can reach down to the horizon and it seemed worth while to use them in an attempt to get colour photographs of the green flash. If these photographs served no other purpose, they would at least demonstrate the objectivity of the phenomenon. This seemed all the more desirable as no colour photographs of the green flash have ever been published, so far as I have been able to discover. Colour photographs of the flash have been taken by DE KEROLYR[142] and HANZAWA,[48] as well as the spectrum photographs studied by JACOBSEN,[56] but no colour reproductions of these have been published.

C. TREUSCH, S. J., of the Observatory staff, who is an experienced photographer, was at first sceptical, realising the difficulty of the task. Later on, however, he took up the idea with enthusiasm and it is entirely due to his skill and patience that the project has succeeded so well. The plan expanded as time went on and many interesting observations were recorded.

Most of the photographs were taken at sunset. For the greater part of the year the sun sets over the Mediterranean, the sea horizon being about 80 km distant for normal refraction (the Observatory is 450 m above sea level). During part of the summer the sun sets behind a land horizon, in the direction of Civitavecchia and over the Tolfa Mountains (90 km distant). The green flash was photographed at sunset over both sea and land.

The green flash at sunrise is a particularly difficult object for colour photography. The telescope must be directed at the precise spot where the flash may appear and one must estimate beforehand the exact instant of appearance and the correct exposure. The task is made more difficult here by the nature of our eastern horizon — the Alban Hills, the lowest point of which is 1° 25′, and the highest (Monte Cavo) 5° 40′ above the astronomical horizon. The distance of the horizon varies from about 4 km to 10 km. Most of the horizon line is covered with forest. At one

point (Rocca Priora) the horizon is clear and sharp, at an elevation of 1° 45', 10 km distant (p. 37). Most of the sunrise photographs were taken in that direction, which was of course possible
only for a short period of the year.

In this paper we present a selection chosen from many successful colour photographs. The selection has been made with
the aim of illustrating various phenomena that have been observed here.

2. *Telescopes.* The earlier photographs were taken with the
Zeiss 60 cm reflector (f.l. 240 cm, mirrors aluminised). A Leica
camera (without lens), interchangeable with a ground glass screen,
was fitted at the Newtonian focus of the telescope. Guiding during
exposures was done with the finder, fitted with cross-wires and
neutral filter. Other technical details can be seen in the photographs of the equipment (Appendix, p. 147).

The reflector was used in order to make sure that no spurious
colour effects were introduced. When sufficient experience had
been gained with the reflector, some photographs were taken with
the Zeiss 40 cm visual refractor (f.l. 6 m). It was found that the
results were in no way inferior to those obtained with the reflector
and that no spurious effects were introduced by the secondary
spectrum of the objective. This lens, a Zeiss E-objective, is in
fact exceptionally well corrected in the visual region. Various
experiments with focus and exposure times proved that it is possible (within a certain tolerance which can be maintained without
difficulty) to obtain an excellent reproduction of the image seen
visually. The very first photographs taken with the refractor
showed the green and red rim with very fine detail, the setting
of Venus and the green flash at sunrise.

Work with the reflector was hampered by the fact that, when
it was pointed to the western horizon, only part of the main mirror
could be used, the rest being occulted by the wall of the dome.
With the refractor, on the other hand, a completely unobstructed
view could be had right to the horizon. Furthermore, the greater
focal length was advantageous for many purposes. All the later
photographs have been taken with the 40 cm refractor, or with
auxiliary telescopes on the same mounting.

3. *Film and Development.* The first tests were made on pan-
chromatic film. In June 1954 the first colour photographs were
taken on Kodachrome 35 mm film. A great deal of experimenting
was needed before the correct exposure times could be found.

The necessity of sending the film to the USA, or to France, for processing was an added complication that delayed the work considerably. Test exposures would be taken and one then had to wait several weeks before the film was returned. In the meantime many good opportunities for observing (in the best season of the year) were lost. As soon as Kodak Ektachrome roll film became available in Italy it was used almost exclusively, on account of the very great advantage that it could be developed here with a Kodak processing kit. All the Ektachrome photographs reproduced here (roll or sheet film, for daylight or for artificial light), as well as all the enlargements, were developed in the Vatican Observatory by C. TREUSCH, with the utmost care and following exactly the Kodak instructions.

Colour negative film was also used at times (plates XI and XII).*

At the beginning or end of many of the colour films used for the flash, exposures were made of a colour scale in full sunlight, in order to provide a control for exact processing.

4. *Exposure Times.* In the last five minutes before sunset the brightness of the sun often falls off markedly as it nears the horizon. This appears, e.g., in the sequence on Plate XVII (in which the green flash on the horizon was slightly under-exposed). In the sequence on Plate I the exposure time was uniform for all the pictures during these last five minutes. This exposure was correct only during the last 15 seconds of sunset, but incorrect for the previous exposures, so that what was observed visually as an intense green appears on the film " washed out " through strong over-exposure.

Estimation of the approximate expected intensity of a flash. It would be hard to find a more incalculable object for a colour photo than a green flash on the horizon, if one aims at reproducing the fine details seen with a focal length of 6 metres. The task is made still more difficult by the fact that only a few seconds are available for moving the film, fixing of exposure time, changing diaphragms, centring exactly on the small focussing screen of the camera by observing on the cross-wires in the guiding telescope, and at the same time taking care to avoid vibrations that

---

* " Color negative materials have somewhat more latitude than reversal films, particularly on the overexposure side. For best results, however, they must be exposed with considerably more care than black-and-white films ".[309]

would ruin photographs taken with such a long focal length. A standard moving-picture camera is of only limited utility on account of the small picture size and other difficulties.

Help in estimating beforehand the correct exposure time for a green flash at sunset can be obtained by observing closely the lower rim of the sun during the few seconds before it touches the horizon (in this case the 80 km distant sea horizon). The changes in this rim enable one to get some idea as to the behaviour of the green flash that will appear in the same layers of the atmosphere about three minutes later. One can for example determine the existence and position of a thin layer of discontinuity immediately above the line of the horizon, perhaps also of a thin layer of haze or of several layers of varying thickness.

All these circumstances may lead, for instance, to the appearance some seconds before sunset of a faint detached green strip high above the horizon, and to a noticeably brighter flash directly on the horizon (or vice versa, depending on haze between observer and very distant horizon, scintillation, mirages, temperature inversions).

Chronograph. It often happened that exposures were made in more or less rapid sequence during a sunset. A lead was taken from each camera to the barrel chronograph of the Observatory, so that the times of the exposures could be recorded. A mean-time signal (from a mean-time clock controlled daily by radio time-signals) was recorded at the end of each sequence, to facilitate the making of whatever small clock corrections were necessary.

5. *Effects of Over- and Under-exposure*. When a colour photograph of the low sun, with a focal length of 6 metres, is correctly exposed, the sky background is always greatly under-exposed. This cannot be avoided. The sky background has very different effects on colour film according to the meteorological conditions between us and the 80 km distant horizon and also beyond the horizon. Haze, that appears white visually, is usually reddish on the film, as also are the edges of bright white clouds near the sun.

This question of the effects of over- or under-exposure is so important that I referred to the Kodak Research Laboratories, Rochester, N.Y., certain conclusions that we had reached, and certain specific questions, for their expert comment and advice. I am very grateful for the trouble that has been taken to deal with my queries. Our observations, listed below, have been completely confirmed by the Research Laboratories; I quote also from the replies to my questions. Kodak sent a wedge spectrogram and processed control strip on Ektachrome sheet film, which were used in studying these points and which are mentioned in the replies.

a) The green rim of the (yellow) setting sun becomes yellow through over-exposure, and thus disappears completely by lack of contrast with the yellow disc of the sun. A blue rim above a white sun becomes white through over-exposure and is thus lost. (Both observations confirmed by the wedge spectrogram). When the exposure was varied, within certain limits, a change from green to blue was never observed, or vice versa (provided that scintillation was not pronounced).

b) There may at times be a superposition (or mixing) of colours during an exposure. This could occur when there is a rapid coarse-grained scintillation along the sun's rim, and at the same time less intense light and consequently longer exposures ($> 1/20$ sec). For example, what colour should Ektachrome Film show at a point where, within this period, the colour changes suddenly from yellow to green, or vice versa? *Reply:* " The color in the reproduction would be intermediate to that obtained in the two cases had the change not occurred during exposure. If the original green color is reproduced as a yellow, and the original yellow is reproduced as a yellow, then the fact that there is a color change during exposure would not influence the color of the reproduction, yellow. However, if the original green were reproduced as green, and the original yellow reproduced as yellow, then, if the color changes during the exposure, the reproduced color would be a greenish yellow, or possibly just yellow ".

c) What would be the effect if the colour changes from blue to green, or vice versa? *Reply:* " Again an intermediate color should result ".

d) Is it ever possible that, through some cause or other (excluding faults in development), an intense green or blue-green should show on Ektachrome Daylight as an intense red? *Reply:* " If by ' intense' green or blue-green is meant ' highly saturated ', then the answer is ' No '. However, if by ' intense ' green is meant ' bright ', but desaturated, green, such an appearance may result from simultaneous contrast rather than from the actual physical make-up of the illumination, and this, combined with normal neutral-scale variability of the film, may result in a bright greenish appearing original being reproduced as a reddish ".

e) " The effect of under and over exposure on the reproduction of colors may be considered from the point of view of two entirely different types of colors, first, those approaching a neutral such as the neutral scale of the processed control strip, and, second, highly saturated colors approaching the spectral colors illustrated by the wedge spectrogram. In the first case, normal emulsion-to-emulsion variation may result in slightly different shifts in color from over to under exposure. Some emulsions may give slightly magenta under exposures, slightly greenish under exposures, etc. The change in color of saturated colors as a function of exposure does not change appreciably from one emulsion to the next. Such changes are illustrated by the wedge spectrogram. Greens go yellow or white with increasing exposure. Various reds may go yellow or magenta..., and various blues may go cyan or magenta ".

6. *Making Colour Movies of Scintillation on the Sun's Rim during Sunset.* It is particularly interesting to take, simultaneously with visual observations, rapid cinematographic photos of the very fine green strips detached from the top of the sun's rim, often mixed up with changing types of scintillation (cf p. 163). These detached strips succeed one another at first very quickly, but more and more slowly as the sun sinks lower (cf p. 152). It is hardly possible to get anything of value with a focal length of less than 6 metres. Tests made at the end of 1954 showed that the following special precautions must be taken: The vertical oscillations of the upper rim of the sun, which increase in range as the sun sinks deeper into layers of discontinuity, are sometimes so marked that precise control of the guiding on the crosswires becomes impossible for minutes on end. The only remedy is to keep the sun's rim centred, as far as possible, in the frame of the cine-camera, by means of the electric fine motions in RA and declination. It requires a certain amount of practice to manage this, especially when the motion is jerky (due to the effect of reflections). These movements (caused by discontinuity layers, varying refraction, reflections) are of themselves enough to render impossible an exact, highly magnified reproduction in colour of all the fine details observed during a sunset.

7. *Flashes Produced Artificially.* A chance observation led to

the experiments showing artificial blue and red flashes near layers of discontinuity. The 8° objective prism (60 cm diameter) was lying on its trolley after having been dismounted from the telescope. A ceiling lamp, an opal sphere of about 20 cm diameter, was seen reflected weakly in the prism. The observer, C. TREUSCH, was greatly struck by the astonishing likeness to the green and red rim of the sun and made some further experiments. A glass mirror was placed under the prism and three panes of ordinary window glass were placed above the prism and slightly inclined to the horizontal. The reflected image of the lamp was now remarkably like the sun's image when distorted by inversion layers. A series of photographs was then taken, as illustrated in Plate XXII and described in the appendix (pp. 153, 159). At the time these experiments were made we were not yet aware of the experiments made by Lord RAYLEIGH.[112, 113]

8. *Reproduction Technique.* Most of the colour photographs, even when the exposure times are correct, are not suitable for high magnification on account of the delicacy of the colours (very small in area). In spite of many interesting details (particularly scintillation) their reproduction has in general not been attempted. In some cases, however, these difficult photographs have been reproduced, in colour or black-and-white; details are given with each photograph.

The firm making the reproductions was instructed to tolerate a loss of delicate tones rather than to reproduce them falsely. This loss has been compensated to some extent by additional description in the text accompanying the pictures.

All colour photographs that were to be reproduced were without exception first enlarged on colour film. When making the Ektachrome enlargements an arrangement was used similar to that recommended by Kodak for making duplicates on Kodachrome.[311] A Zeiss-Tessar lens was used, with a Nitraphot lamp as light source. Exposures, with the usual Kodak Color Compensating Filters, were not longer than 30 seconds. The enlargements were placed on a sheet of glass, as they will appear on the printed page, then covered with a second glass plate and the edges bound with scotch tape. The reproductions were made from these enlargements, in the same size. During the process of reproduction the valuable original films were used only to control the final colours. The adjustment of the colours in the print so as to reproduce the colours of the original as closely as possible was not always easy.* It must be borne in mind that a great deal of the brilliance of the original colour film is unavoidably lost in a paper print.**

Experts in scientific colour photography will doubtless be able to suggest various improvements in the technique to be employed in a research of this kind. If our photographs induce some of the experts to follow up our studies of these phenomena, so much the better. It is well, however, to stress the following point. If the results are to be exploited to the full, it is necessary that a sequence of colour photos of the green flash, or of scintillation, be accompanied by visual observations at the telescope, which should be compared with the photographs on the same day, or as soon as possible, while the visual impressions are still fresh.

9. *Arrangement of the Photographs*. It was not easy to decide how best to group the photographs. When they are arranged chronologically it is easy to follow the influence of meteorological conditions on the appearance of the sun's rim, especially when pictures are taken on successive days. If, on the other hand, the pictures are grouped according to different types of observations, this time sequence is to some extent upset. It was finally decided to divide the photographs into three main groups, corresponding broadly to different ways in which the green flash may develop, while at the same time preserving the time sequence as far as practicable. It is believed that in this way a fairly clear and coherent view of the various phenomena is provided. The grouping is as follows: A) *The Green Rim;* B) *The Green Segment with*

---

* " The colors seen in a transparency depend strongly on the viewing light, and it is not enough for them to be pleasant to look at ".[310] " As compared with transparencies for projection, Kodachrome transparencies for reproduction by photomechanical methods of color-printing should have slightly less exposure, and both subject contrast and lighting contrast should be softer. The most satisfying results are obtained when the photographer works in close co-operation with the photomechanical worker who is to reproduce the Kodachrome transparencies ".[312]

** " A photograph, whether black-and-white or coloured, viewed by transmitted light is far richer in intermediate tones than one viewed by reflected light. In a transparency the extreme range of tones is in a ratio of about 1 to 1,000, whereas in a paper print the very best that can be hoped for is a ratio of 1 to 50. Thus transparencies always appear very much more brilliant than prints " (translated from the Italian).[308] " In comparison to a positive color transparency viewed on a light box, even the finest color print seems flat and dull ".[313]

Green Flash; C) *The Green and the Red Flash Influenced by Discontinuity Layers.* Some sunset sequences contain characteristics of more than one group, so that the division cannot be clear-cut, but it is hoped that this will not cause confusion. Plate I, which shows the influence of various factors on the development of a green flash, is printed as a frontispiece.

In the text accompanying the photographs are meteorological and other data and accounts of relevant observations. The technique was, however, developed gradually, so that less complete data are available for the earlier pictures.

In the Appendix are given details of the technical equipment; meteorological notes; experiments on artificial sunsets; examples of scintillation effects; examples of effects of incorrect exposure in colour photography.

Acknowledgments

I have to thank many friends, astronomers and other scientists, for their encouragement and for the interest they have taken in this work. In particular I must express my grateful appreciation for helpful discussions and advice to Professor D. H. MENZEL, Director, Harvard Observatory; Professor M. G. J. MINNAERT, Director, Utrecht Observatory (whose fascinating book " *Light and Colour in the Open Air* " has been for years past a constant stimulus and source of interest); Dr. H. J. SMITH, Sacramento Peak Observatory, New Mexico; and Professor S. W. VISSER, Meteorologisch Instituut, De Bilt. I must also thank the Kodak Research Laboratories, Rochester, N. Y., and particularly Dr. W. T. HANSON Jr., who prepared the report quoted in the text; Major General LIBRI, Capo del Servizio Meterologico, Ministero della Difesa-Aeronautica, who kindly supplied radiosonde observations from Ciampino and Elmas; the Schweizerische Meteorologische Zentralanstalt, Zürich, for supplying many weather maps. Much time and great care and skill were devoted to the printing of the colour plates – by ENRICO LODOLI, Rome, who prepared the plates for printing (in six colours by offset process), and by the printers, the Tipografia Poliglotta Vaticana. The photographs themselves are sufficient evidence of how much is owing to the skill and devoted labour of C. TREUSCH, S. J.

A. The Green Rim

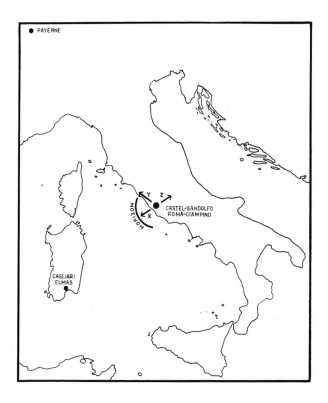

The sketch shows the directions of sunset and sunrise as observed from the Vatican Observatory, Castel Gandolfo (altitude 450 m in the Alban Hills). Between X and Y there is for the most part a sea horizon. In direction Z, about 100 km away, lie the Apennines.

In Part A are photographs (1) of the green rim in general, and (2) of the green rim in contact with the horizon. In connection with group (2) various observations were made on the effects of local refraction, diffraction, nearby or distant scintillation, etc, and the Plates have been grouped (roughly) according to the type of observation. A few pictures of the setting Moon and planets supplement the observations of the sun's rim. Several of the above-mentioned effects are also illustrated in many other photographs in Parts B and C and in the Appendix.

Average Vertical Extension of the Green Rim at Sunrise and Sunset

In a miniature camera or standard cine-camera, without a telephoto lens, the diameter of the sun's image is about 0.5 mm. The vertical extension of the top of the green rim is hardly more than about 0.005 mm, and that of a green flash on the horizon often not much greater. It is not surprising then that the film shows no trace of a flash, even when it appears brilliant to the naked eye[8]. With a focal length of 240 cm the width of the green rim is somewhat more than 0.2 mm, but even then it will often be impossible to reproduce in colour many of the details shown on the original film. A focal length of at least 6 metres is required in order to obtain reproducible colour photographs which will show, for instance, the fine details of scintillation. One might of course try to use instruments of shorter focal length, with auxiliary optics to increase the size of the focal image, but it would probably be very difficult to avoid spurious colours, produced by the additional lens or lenses, which would be superimposed on the colours which it is sought to reproduce, rendering photographs of the green flash of no real value.

The inner edge of the green rim is sometimes over-exposed, and the outer portion under-exposed, so that its full width is not always shown in a colour photograph. A better estimate can be obtained by direct observation. The measures in the following table were made visually by C. TREUSCH in two different ways, almost simultaneously with photographs of the green rim. a) With guiding telescope (f.l. 1 m) and neutral filter. In the focal plane of the eyepiece was fixed a scale, consisting of a series of calibrated slits of different widths, in which the upper part of the sun's rim could be centred. b) By way of control a similar ' slit scale ' was used, in rapid succession, on the 6 m refractor. The (movable) scale was attached to a fine-grained ground-glass screen. The sun's image (about 55 mm in diameter), focussed on the screen, was viewed at slightly oblique incidence; in this way it is possible to observe even a faint green rim. A very diffuse, faint blue glow, sometimes seen near the outer edge of the green rim (when about 3° above the horizon)[44], was not included in the measured width.

Changes in the Green Rim

It is not easy to note the multifarious fine variations in colour, intensity, extent, influence of scintillation (whether slight or marked or of different types). These effects are often seen to be stratified. At other times they appear in indescribable confusion, sometimes one type and sometimes another predominating. The following table shows how visual observations during a sequence of photographs were rapidly noted down (in order to compare the photographs with the image seen visually).

The symbols used in the table of zenith distances (pp. 99, 100) are used also here, with the same significance, except that they refer to the green rim at a given height above the horizon. Additional symbols refer to the very fine green strips that are often detached from the upper rim of the sun, either in single (m) or in multiple (m') layers (cf pictures on pp. 161, 162). p — indicates that very fine green spikes are beginning to form (p. 61); p' — denotes coarser spikes, and pr — green spikes with very short horizontal red streaks in between.

For example: Y g s⁰ p' m 10″-20″ signifies: Sun yellow, rim emerald green, almost no scintillation, very fine green spikes forming on the upper rim and disappearing as simple detached green strips; the top of the green rim is 10″-20″ broad.

It is to be noted that, as the sun nears the horizon, estimates of the width of the green rim often become more uncertain, on account of the influence of (more or less fine) layers of discontinuity and of reflections.

Sunset Date	Loc. temp.	Rel. humid.	Loc. wind	Seeing to horizon	Zenith distance of the sun's upper limb						
					87⁰	87.5⁰	88⁰	88.5⁰	89⁰	89.5⁰	90⁰
1957	°C	%									
March 13	8	55	w⁰	z′s⁰		4″-17″ Y bg s⁰ p pr	10″-20″ Y bg ts′		20″-25″ OR h′ g t′ s′ p″ m		25″-45″ OR h′ g t″ s⁰ p″ m′
March 14	9	60	w⁰	z′s′	4″-7″ s′ bg	7″ s′ bg	7″-10″ Y s⁰ bg p′		10″-15″ YO h′ g s′ p′		15″-25″ OR h′ g s′ p″ m′
March 16	9	40	w⁰	z⁰s⁰	4″-7′ s⁰ b		7″-10″ s⁰ b	7″-10″ s⁰ b p m	10″-15″ Y bg p′ ts′ m′		15″-20″ OR h′ g t′ s⁰ p″ m
March 19	11	50	w⁰	z⁰s⁰	4″-7″ s⁰ b			4″-7″ s⁰ b p′	7″-10″ Y s⁰ bg p′		10″-20″ OR h′ g s⁰ p′ m

Lowest point of eastern horizon as seen from Castel Gandolfo.
In the foreground is the tube of the 6 metre refractor. The photograph was taken a few seconds before the appearance of the first rays of the rising sun (June 6, 1955) with Leica camera. In the lower photograph one can see the same spot after sunrise. The arrow indicates the summit of the mountain where the rising sun appears in the following pictures

Focus test exposure on colour film
Photograph of the rising sun with the 2.4 metre reflector (Newtonian focus), aperture stopped down to about 5 cm. Taken on Ferraniacolor neg. with Leica camera. Exposure 1/1000 sec. Enlarged in black and white. Fine details 10 km away are easily visible in the original photographs directly in front of the sun's disc. The sharp outlines of the medieval castle on the summit of the mountain are seen very highly enlarged in the four following plates of colour photographs on Reversal film.

PLATE II   41

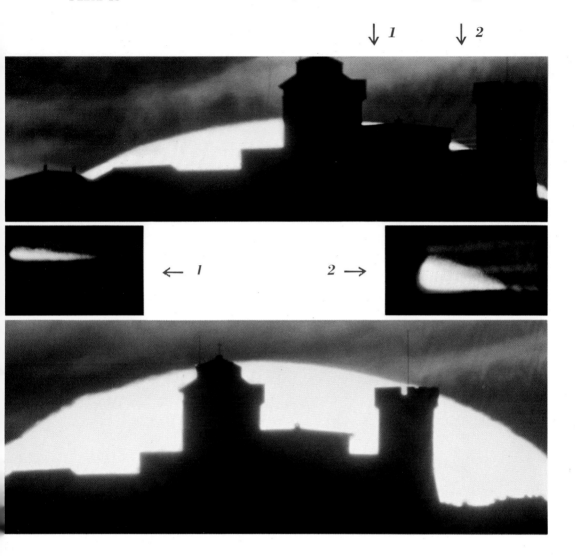

July 12, 1955 – Sunrise at the same spot with green flashes (1) and (2) at a distance of 10 km. Note that the green of the right hand flash (2) is divided by a telephone or electric wire. The rest of the sun's rim was also green but much fainter and thus lost with this magnification. At this sunrise no scintillation was observed. Temp. 19°C, rel. humid. 40%, no wind. Photographs taken with 40 cm refractor on Ektachrome daylight about 1/100 sec., enlarged 4.4× (middle picture 12×).

PLATE III

43

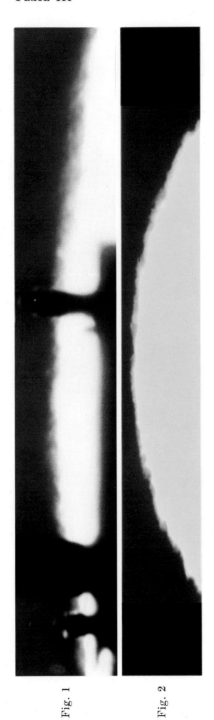

Fig. 1

Fig. 2

The blue and the green rim, with scintillation effects in colour.

Fig. 1 – Sunrise July 15, 1954 – The sun's disc was observed visually in the guide telescope as white with a brilliant blue rim. The air and the 10 km distant horizon were very steady, but the sun's rim was scintillating rapidly in a particular direction. Taken on Kodachrome daylight 1/1000 sec. Sun's diameter 70 cm. Local temp. 21°C, rel. humid. 65%.

Fig. 2 – Sunset Aug. 8, 1954 – The sun's disc was observed visually as yellow with an intense green rim about 9 minutes before sunset when the photograph was taken. The seeing was good near the horizon (some distant cloud), light SE wind in the morning and light N wind at sunset. There was from time to time on the rim a strange mixture of green scintillation and long sharp green spikes, impossible to reproduce in detail. Local. temp. 23°C, rel. humid. 65% Film: Agfacolor T, enlarged 4.4×. All photographs taken with 40 cm refractor (f. l. 6 metre) with Leica.

Green Flashes at Sunrise

When the scintillation was extremely feeble and the sun rose with a hardly perceptible blue-green rim, at many points very intense blue-green flashes were seen in the guiding telescope. It was observed that under these atmospheric conditions the contours of the horizon exerted a marked influence. In the following three colour plates some of these sunrises are shown, with various relevant data. The exposures, taken with the 6 m refractor, are very greatly enlarged (although with some disadvantages) in order to reproduce these effects sufficiently clearly for publication. The following remarks apply to plate IV:

At many points very intense green flashes were seen before the first appearance of the rim. It is not quite correct to say that they appeared " before " the rim, for, wherever the green shows, the sun's rim seems to be momentarily held back regard to the rising edge of the sun's disc (middle photograph); then it suddenly shoots upwards and at the same instant the green disappears (upper photograph). This phenomenon, which in the picture is seen over a fairly extended horizontal line, is repeated on a smaller scale in dozens of places where humps appear (plate V). Above these humps the sun's rim seems pinched in, when the green appears at these points.

" Hump-effects " similar to those in this sunrise are sometimes seen at sunset, especially when there is a green flash in the form of a strip in direct contact with the 80 km distant sea horizon. Even when there is very little scintillation, it looks sometimes as if the sea waves cause an effect similar to the " humps " on this eastern horizon-line and by their motion simulate a strong scintillation (green and blue-green), which is in fact absent (see flash on plate XII).

PLATE IV 47

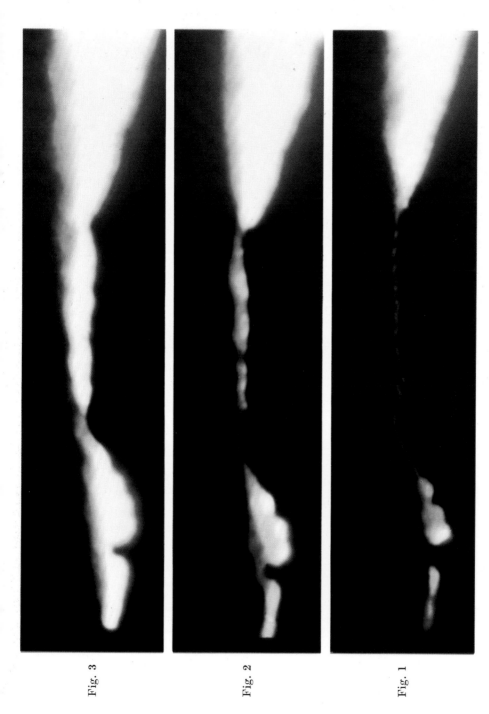

Fig. 3

Fig. 2

Fig. 1

July 17, 1956 – Green flashes at sunrise. Effects of local refractions on the line of the horizon. Taken with ROBOT-Stern camera in the focus of the 40 cm refractor (f.l. 6 metre), stopped down to 10 cm. Time intervals about 0.5 sec. Exposure time 1/250 sec. on Ektachrome daylight. Enlarged 23.7 ×. See other notes on page 45.

PLATE V   49

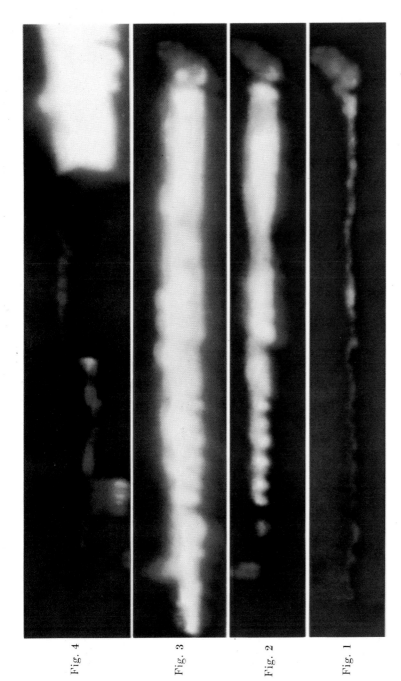

Fig. 4

Fig. 3

Fig. 2

Fig. 1

July 17, 1955 – Cinematographic exposures of the first rays of the rising sun, highly magnified (18.5 ×). Note the first green flash in figure 1 at the 10 km distant horizon. Less than one second later there was observed visually a chain of several blue-green and yellow points, which changed into peculiar diffuse green vertical lines above the nearest points of the horizon (fig. 2). About one second later they had vanished (fig. 3). This phenomenon seems to

be quite distinct from the green rim of the sun, which was extremely faint on this occasion. When the telescope was moved to another, slightly higher, point of the very irregular horizon, another green flash was observed some seconds later (fig. 4).

Taken with 40 cm refractor (f.l. 6 metre), stopped down to 10 cm, 1/100 sec. on Ektachrome daylight.

Local temp. 19°C, rel. humid. 70%, no scintillation.

➡

In this sunrise the cusps of the rising segment were an intense green. As soon as the upper edge of the (white) sun was clear of the very irregular 10 km distant horizon, the rim was seen to be blue. The photographs were taken July 7, 1956 with ROBOT-camera, two pictures per second, 1/250 sec. exp. (6m f. l., aperture 40 cm, stopped down to 10 cm). Film: Ektachrome B. Enlargement: sun's diameter 132 cm. Height of the horizon above astronomical horizon 1°25′. No wind and no scintillation. Local temp. 21°C.

PLATE VI   51

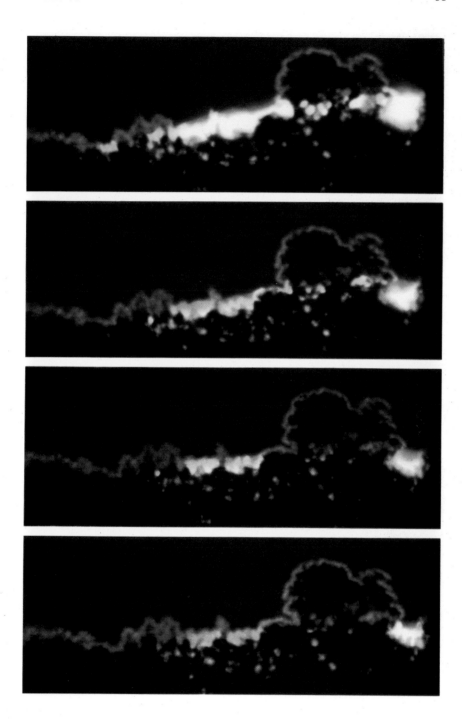

Plate VII   53

Fig. 1

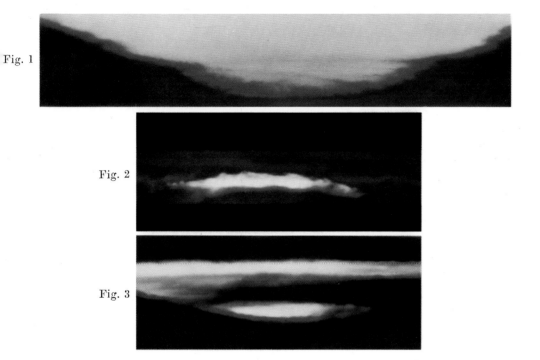

Fig. 2

Fig. 3

The green flash above a cloudbank.

Fig. 2 and 3 – Sunset Aug. 8, 1954 – The two photographs were taken some 15 seconds apart, about 11 minutes before sunset. The upper rim of the sun disappeared with a green flash, disturbed by scintillation (fig. 2). The lower rim reappeared beneath the very distant cloud with a sharp-lined red rim without any scintillation effects (fig. 3).

Fig. 1 – Sunset Aug. 11, 1954 – shows fine structure in a red rim about 1°.5 above horizon. No scintillation. No wind. Local temp. 23ºC, rel. humid. 50%.

All three photographs were taken with 40 cm refractor (f. l. 6 metre), 1/1000 sec exposure times with Leica-camera on Agfacolor T, enlarged 4.4 ×.

Photographs of diffraction effects at a distant horizon.

Sunrise, seen from Castel Gandolfo, taken on Ektachrome daylight. At left of the upper picture the wire fence of a 10 km distant meadow shows the sunlight strongly diffracted. On the right, still before sunrise, the trees are surrounded by a brilliant silvery white radiance. When the exposure time is suitable for photographs of the green rim of the rising sun these diffraction effects on the trees are underexposed. Thus a colour photograph often does not represent what the eye sees in the guide telescope as a " silvery white ". The under-exposure changes this white to a more or less dark yellow near the correctly exposed green or blue rim on the white sun. The amount of this change depends very much on scintillation and on the atmospheric conditions between observatory and horizon (note also p. 51).

The interval between the commencement of this diffracted light and the appearance of the sun's rim is not always the same. In any case it is a considerable help in finding rapidly the exact point of the horizon where the rim of the sun will appear. On this day the air was very pure and there was no scintillation on the horizon.

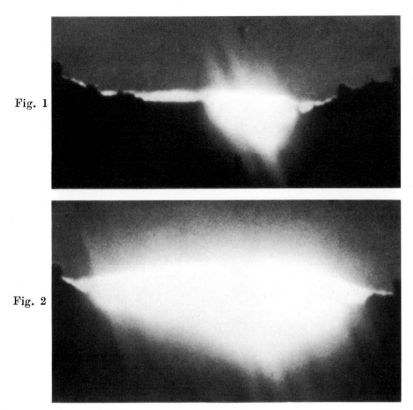

Fig. 1

Fig. 2

Fig. 1 and 2 – A slight increase of exposure sometimes brings out " ray effects "
on sharp details of a 10 km distant horizon, as seen in this sunrise. In the Ektachrome
photographs they appeared a faint red-yellow on the white disc of the sun. Evidently this colour is caused by the same under-exposure as the red-yellow in the
diffraction effects on pages 51, 55.

Fig. 3

Fig. 3 – When the sun's rim is " shooting " out of the horizon in this (highly magnified) form, the naked eye seems to see a green " ray ". In this photograph, taken
with a focal length of 6 metres, there is nothing like a " ray " or " flame " but rather
the motion of green strips, disappearing within a second or two.

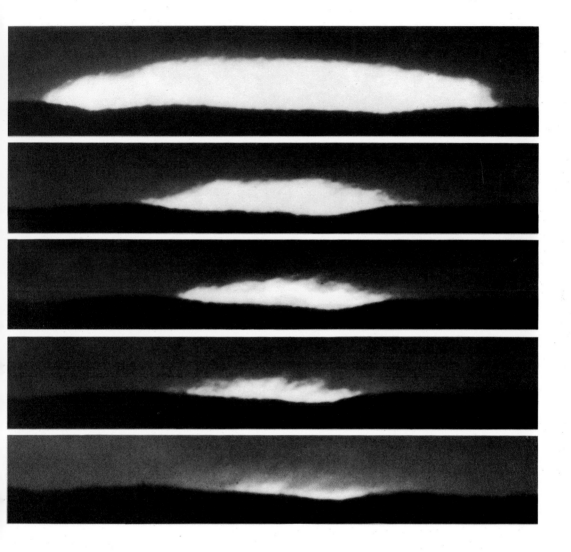

May 20, 1956 – This red sunset behind the 90 km distant Tolfa mountains appeared
without any green. The last rays look like a forest fire in a high wind, whereas the
local weather conditions were moderately calm. Similar " flames ", but green and
much smaller, can sometimes be observed on the sun's rim, shooting in a preferred
direction and mixed with scintillation. Taken with the 6 m refractor on Ektachrome.

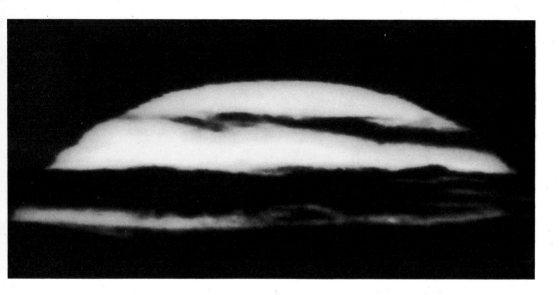

Spikes on the green rim about 15 minutes before sunset.
In this case (March 22, 1954) the very distant clouds had no observable effect on the sun's rim. The cause of the spikes must be much further off and at a great altitude, as Wegener also supposes. They are sometimes so fine that a reproduction is difficult (in colour). See an example in black-and-white in Appendix on p. 158. When there is strong scintillation in the lower atmosphere the fine spikes can sometimes be seen to vanish gradually. Note in the photographs below (Nov. 26, 1955) at left a prominent spike on the upper rim and the scintillation effect on the lower rim. Three minutes later the upper rim also entered this strong scintillation layer and all spikes disappeared (figure at right). Note the simultaneous vertical elongation of the sun's disc. Other pictures of this sunset are on pages 95, 162, 163.

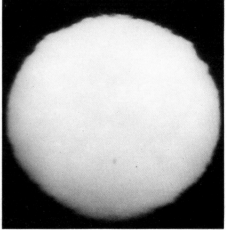

Influence of the upper atmosphere ?   ➡
On many occasions the sun's rim is very disturbed compared with the sharp outline
of a very distant horizon in the same line of sight. In these photographs is shown
such a sunset on May 10, 1955 (behind the highest part of the "Isola del Giglio"
498 m, 160 km away). Taken with the 6 m refractor.

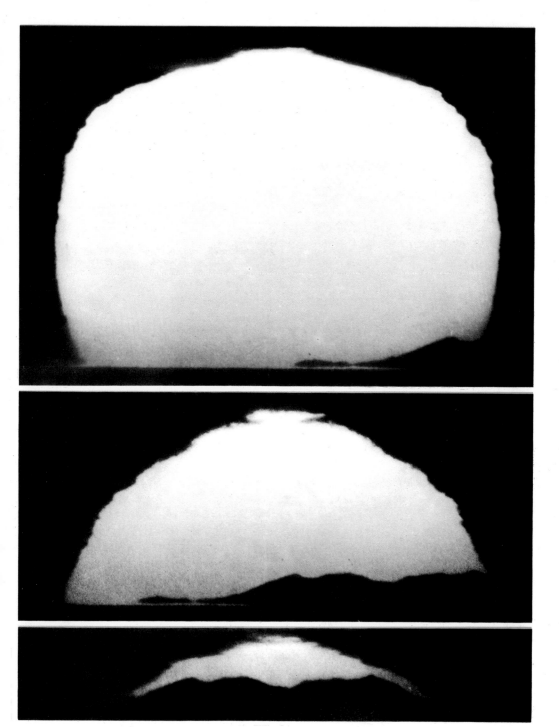

PLATE VIII   65

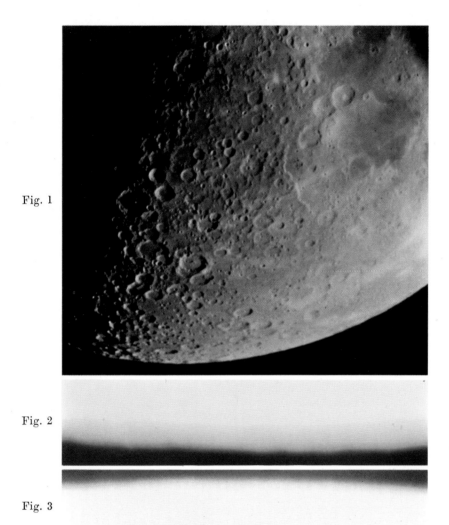

Fig. 1

Fig. 2

Fig. 3

July 16, 1954 – The green and the red rim of the setting Moon. Fig. 1 is in the same focus as fig. 2 and 3, there is a difference only in exposure times and height above horizon. In the two lower photographs the moon's disc is a clear yellow colour, due to the overexposure, which was needed in order to show the red and green rim. To facilitate comparison of the colours, the two rims are juxtaposed, with the lower rim above. Taken with 40 cm refractor (f.l. 6 m), on Kodachrome.

PLATE IX   67

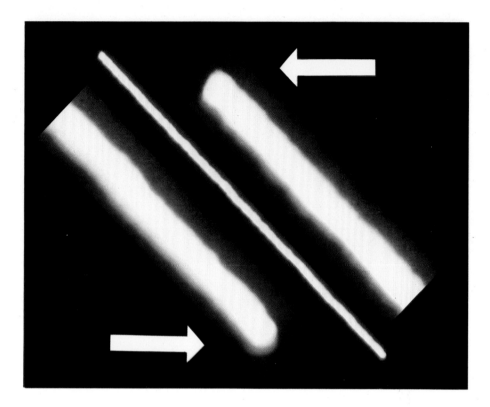

Photographs of Venus near the horizon, telescope fixed.

July 10, 1954 – Note influence of fine layers of discontinuity. They caused small deviations in the trail. Simultaneously there appear very fine green flashes, vertically elongated, too faint for colour photographs. But there remains a trace of them in a more or less intense green rim. Arrows show this green and red rim at the beginning (top) and end (below) of exposure.

There was very little scintillation and a clear horizon. The photograph was begun 16 minutes before the planet disappeared. The colour of the planet changed from white through yellow (when the photograph was taken) to orange and red. The inclination of the trail to the horizontal in the photograph corresponds to the inclination of the ecliptic.

Taken with 40 cm refractor (f. l. 6 metre) on Gevaertcolor Reversal with Leica-camera, enlarged (left and right hand image) 23.7 ×.

The middle picture shows the trail for about 60 seconds enlarged 4.4 ×.

(For other notes see page 152.)

Plate X   69

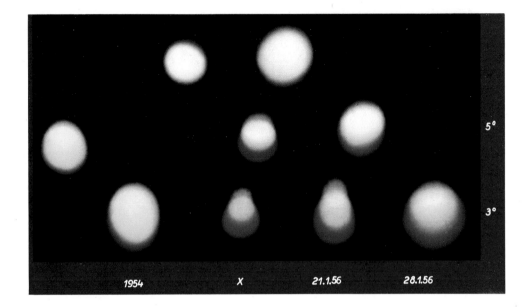

Photographs of Venus near the horizon, telescope guided in RA and dec.

In each series the sequence of photographs follows the line of the ecliptic (as previous plate). Note the increasing dispersion. In mid-July Venus was 13″ in diameter and 83% illuminated, magnitude –3.4. All photographs were taken with 40 cm refractor (f.l. 6 m) and enlarged 23.7 ×.

28.6.1954 – The two photographs in the lower left hand corner were selected from several exposures on Ferraniacolor Invertibile (daylight). The upper picture was taken with about 3 seconds, lower picture with about 30 seconds exposure. The meteorological conditions were not good, some haze near the horizon, no wind but some scintillation. Several hours later the rel. humidity had reached 90%. A distinct green rim was observed, but no blue rim, when the photographs were taken.

21.1.1956 – The evening was clear with very little scintillation.
The three exposure times were 0.5 sec. 2 sec. 10 sec. Note the increasing dispersion which during the 10 sec. exposure was about twice as great visually as appears in the photograph. It seems to be like a continuous spectrum from deep red through orange, yellow, green and a very elongated blue, sometimes interrupted by dark lines, corresponding evidently to the fine layers of discontinuity. These appeared and vanished with a frequency which varied with the height above horizon. The photograph marked X, with only 3 sec. exposure, shows the faint green better, while the blue is underexposed and is lost in the photograph. In the 10 sec. exposure this green seems to be overexposed and thus fused with yellow (see Appendix page 173).
Photographs taken on Ektachrome daylight, magnified on Ektachrome B, rel. humid. 70%, local temp. 8°C, no wind.

28.1.1956 – Note influence of very strong scintillation. Seeing very good near the horizon. Local temp. 3°C. Rel. humid. 40%. Light N wind.
Taken on Ektachrome daylight and enlarged on Ektachrome B like the preceding series to facilitate a comparison.

B. The Green Segment with Green Flash

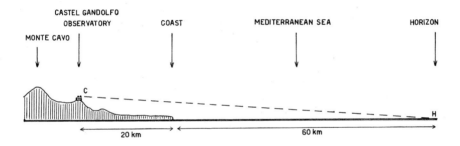

A distant horizon is needed in order to obtain photographs of the green segment. How favourable the Castel Gandolfo site is in this respect can be seen from the above profile. The line of sight to the western horizon, CH, is, with mean refraction, at least 80 km. H is for most of the year the Mediterranean Sea, and in summer the low Tolfa Mountains (about 90 km distant).

The next series of plates begins with a sunset over these mountains, showing particularly clearly the development of the green segment. Then follow photographs of the green segment on the sea horizon, with various colour effects. Finally, some black-and-white enlargements give an idea of the marked influence that atmospheric conditions have on the fine details of the last light of the setting sun.

Plate XI   73

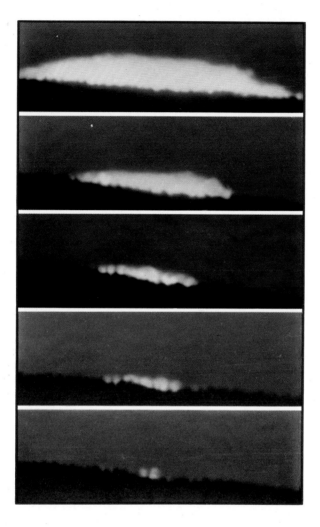

The green flash above 90 km distant mountains.

June 13, 1954 – Sunset was behind the Tolfa Mountains near Civitavecchia, about 500 m in height, easily visible from Castel Gandolfo. The sun's disc was a paler yellow than usual. Note the last segment which became green at the extremities. The green then shifted gradually towards the centre of the segment. The last flash was a pure emerald green. Photographs were exposed 1/20 sec. with Leica-camera. Taken with the 60 cm reflector (f.l. 2.4 m) stopped down to about 30 cm. Film: Ferraniacolor neg. 23, enlargement 7 ×.

Local temp. 21°C, rel. humid. 50%, seeing clear near the horizon but some haze in the upper strata of the atmosphere. Little scintillation.

The sky background in the last two photos is somewhat brighter than in the others, due to a slight increase in exposure when making the enlargements in order to make the line of the horizon clearer.

PLATE XII   75

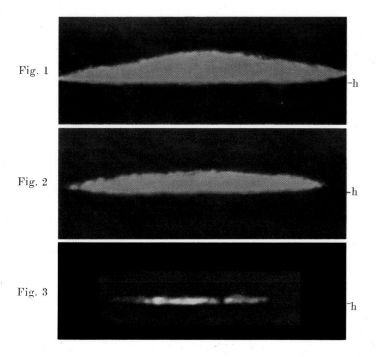

Fig. 1

Fig. 2

Fig. 3

A mixture of green and blue flash at the sea horizon.

Aug. 12, 1954 – The sunset was taken with the 60 cm reflector. Note the upturned corners in fig. 1 and 2, with a little green at the extremities (in fig. 2). Note also in this photograph the sea horizon *h*, about 80 km distant, contrasting with the very disturbed blue flash in fig. 3.

There was little scintillation. The sun was orange-yellow. The colour of the flash twinkled, from green and some yellow in the centre, to blue in the extremities. 1/100 sec. exposure with the Leica-camera. Taken with reflector (f. l. 2.4 metre) stopped down to about 10 cm. Film: Ferraniacolor neg. 23, enlarged 7 ×. Local temp. 20° C, rel. humid. 35%.

PLATE XIII   77

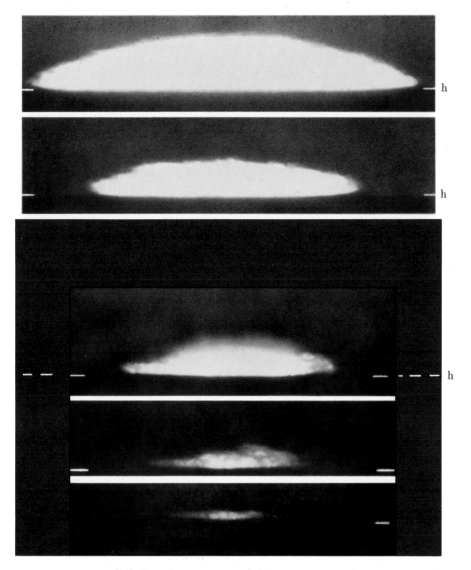

Red rim phenomenon on the green segment.

Nov. 22, 1955 – A strange inversion of the green rim to an intense red rim was photographed during this sunset above the sea. No unusual meteorological conditions were observed. It was clear, with no cloud, no wind.

Note in the middle photograph a trail of red rays in the red rim which seem to start radially from a point below the horizon while the green at the extremities of the segment was boiling with a coarse-grained scintillation, in marked contrast with the much weaker scintillation on the horizon.

(With regard to the reproduction of this series note also page 173). Taken with 40 cm refractor (f. l. 6 metre) on Ektachrome daylight 1/50 sec. enlarged 4.4 ×. Local temp. 6⁰ C, rel. humid. 50%. Radiosonde soundings and other notes see pages 81,83.

PLATE XIV   79

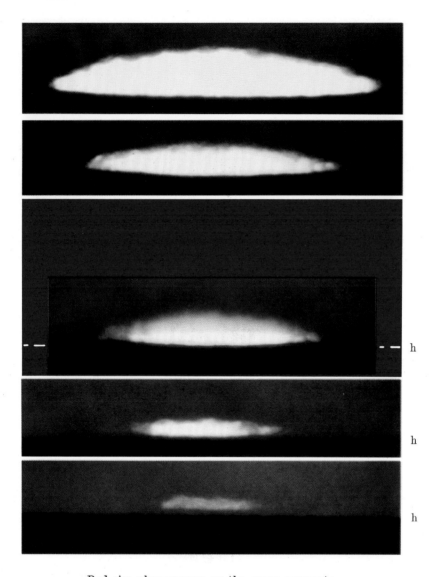

h

h

h

Red rim phenomenon on the green segment.

Sept. 16, 1955 – In this sunset a similar colour effect was photographed as in the preceding series, but less intense. At about the same height above the horizon as on Nov. 22 the colour of the green rim changed for a very short time to red, while the green at the extremities of the segment remained. It is probable that the red was more intense a fraction of a second before or after the exposure. There is also, but less distinct, the same trail of red rays which seem to start radially from a point below the horizon as in the preceding series.

Note the weather conditions before this sunset (page 81).

Taken with 40 cm refractor (f. l. 6 metre) on Ektachrome daylight, 1/50 sec. Local temp. 14°C. Rel. humid. 32%. Light N wind. Enlarged 4.4 ×. Radiosonde soundings see page 82.

81

Notes on the Sunsets with Green and Red Segment
(Plates XIII, XIV)

As this phenomenon occurs rarely, it seems worth while to compare various observations made on these two days. An over-exposure with consequent change in colour (cf pp. 27, 172), caused by a sudden marked brightening of the green of the upper rim, is hardly possible. On Nov. 22 the sunset without any noticeable increase of brightness (as seen with the naked eye). On both days the green flash stood out clearly on the sharp 80 km distant horizon; in the original photos it is rather under- than over-exposed. At these two sunsets the refraction did not differ much from the normal (cf table of sun's zenith distance, p. 99). Note the differences between the weather maps (pp. 82, 83), which provide a wider survey in the observing direction. For the sunsets over the sea we have no radiosonde soundings exactly in the observing direction, but only from a station to the south of that direction (Cagliari-Elmas) and from one to the north (Payerne). Recordings from both these stations are given on this page and the next. The graphs permit a more rapid survey of the meteorological conditions than the more exact, but less easily comparable, tables.

Radiosonde soundings Sept. 16, 1955   Radiosonde soundings Nov. 22, 1955

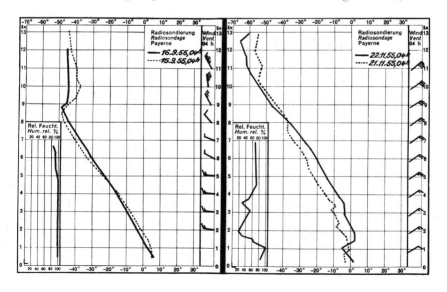

Radiosonde soundings Sept. 16, 1955

Local (Roma-Ciampino)						400 Km distant (Cagliari-Elmas)				
mb	m	°C	wind dir.	vel.		mb	m	°C	wind dir.	vel.
996	104	16,6	220°	08		1000	106	17,4	300°	08
985	220	17,6	240	15		946	580	13,4	320	06
935	650	14,3	250	21		938	660	14,4	320	06
917	820	10,8	240	20	16	900	998	11,6	310	09
850	1437	6,3	250	21	hours	850	1480	9,3	300	15
785	2090	3,5	270	28	before	800	1971	6,5	280	20
755	2400	+ 0,3	280	32	sunset	775	2250	6,5	270	23
700	2999	— 5,2	280	38		700	3069	3,5	250	28
661	3460	— 8,6	280	42		600	4302	— 4,8	260	25
635	3770	— 9,6	260	39		580	4560	— 7,5	260	27
621	3940	— 9,1	250	45		518	5480	— 9,1	260	21
569	4610	—14,0	260	60		500	5752	—11,0	260	26
500	5563	—20,8	260	64						
1002	104	19,6	00	00		1000	144	19,7	330	15
1000	122	18,5	00	00		900	1036	9,4	320	13
895	1070	9,7	350	10	4,5	885	1175	8,7	320	13
850	1486	6,3	360	17	hours	850	1520	9,4	320	19
823	1770	4,2	360	23	before	700	3103	2,9	290	25
802	1980	3,3	350	30	sunset	655	3615	+ 0,9	290	26
700	3044	— 5,0	340	30		628	3990	+ 3,2	280	36
672	3370	— 7,6	330	28		500	5776	— 9,7	310	27
650	3630	— 8,0	330	30						
595	4320	—14,0	330	32						
583	4460	—15,6	330	34						
500	5592	—24,1	330	39						
1009	104	12,0	50	08		1000	187	14,0	00	00
1000	180	15,4	50	09		900	1073	11,3	00	00
968	450	15,8	40	12	7,5	855	1500	8,5	00	00
940	700	13,8	20	13	hours	850	1550	9,1	00	00
850	1548	8,4	360	16	after	800	2043	8,3	290	08
836	1700	7,5	360	17	sunset	785	2200	8,4	290	05
700	3128	1,5	340	22		700	3142	4,9	280	07
665	3550	— 1,7	310	29		650	3750	4,1	280	08
630	3970	— 2,7	300	26		500	5824	—11,1	290	31
593	4450	— 5,6	310	35						
586	4560	— 6,4	310	36						
559	4920	— 4,9	320	35						
500	5778	—10,5	310	41						

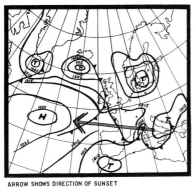

ARROW SHOWS DIRECTION OF SUNSET

11 hours before sunset

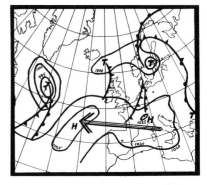

12 hours after sunset

Radiosonde soundings Nov. 22, 1955

Local (Roma-Ciampino) | | | | | | 400 Km distant (Cagliari-Elmas) | | | | |

mb	m	°C	wind dir.	vel.		mb	m	°C	wind dir.	vel.
1008	104	2,4	60°	09		1000	186	10,5	00°	00
1000	169	3,0	60	09		980	360	9,3	00	00
985	300	4,3	50	08		938	725	5,8	00	00
956	530	4,3	120	05		907	995	3,2	00	00
860	1300	— 2,4	320	05	15	865	1390	— 0,1	00	00
850	1479	— 2,4	330	08	hours	850	1511	— 0,6	00	00
843	1520	— 2,4	330	08	before	835	1650	— 0,7	330	06
770	2260	— 6,9	350	17	sunset	820	1810	+ 2,3	310	05
700	2995	—10,3	340	21		788	2125	+ 0,9	310	05
670	3300	—13,0	340	22		757	2445	— 1,0	300	06
656	3480	—13,0	340	23		740	2615	— 1,2	290	05
603	4100	—16,0	360	26		700	3060	— 5,4	270	05
574	4470	—17,5	10	26		627	3910	—11,4	300	10
500	5520	—26,3	10	32		500	5623	—22,5	290	22
1010	104	12,2	40	05		1000	200	12,9	120	05
1000	188	9,5	50	04		876	1300	2,2	250	04
850	1517	1,3	20	08		850	1537	3,0	280	03
750	2530	— 3,4	360	22		818	1860	3,9	310	04
740	2640	— 3,4	360	23	3	700	3094	— 4,0	310	05
700	3064	— 6,0	360	21	hours	648	3680	— 7,0	290	06
690	3190	— 6,0	360	21	before	500	5664	—21,3	290	09
680	3290	— 4,5	360	22	sunset					
615	4080	—10,1	20	23						
604	4200	— 9,4	20	23						
572	4620	—11,0	20	23						
500	5652	—19,6	360	22						
985	104	8,8	60	05		985	180	10,5	310	17
850	1306	0,8	360	03		925	700	6,8	300	24
768	2100	— 5,6	300	05		875	1130	2,6	310	24
760	2200	— 4,1	300	06		850	1366	1,5	310	22
700	2837	— 8,6	280	16	33	790	1950	2,4	300	44
615	3830	—16,8	280	38	hours	765	2210	2,5	290	38
590	4160	—16,8	280	41	after	700	2928	— 1,7	290	50
568	4520	—18,5	280	40	sunset	672	3250	— 3,9	280	44
500	5357	—25,1	270	56		643	3580	— 6,0	290	35
						627	3800	— 8,5	290	28
						537	4990	—16,3	290	50
						500	5506	—20,2	290	40

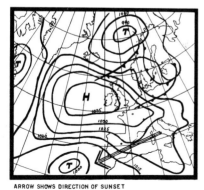

ARROW SHOWS DIRECTION OF SUNSET

9 hours before sunset

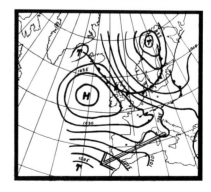

8 hours after sunset

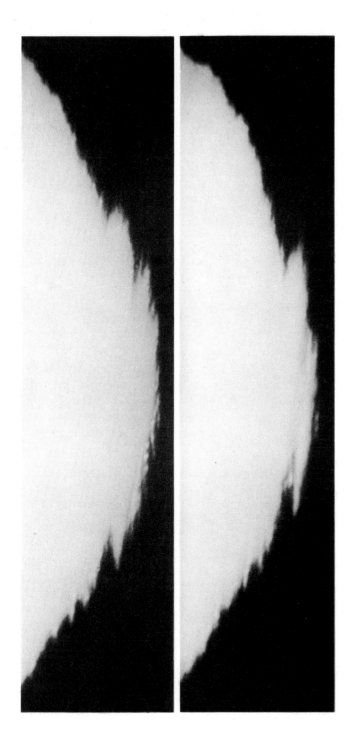

Sunset sequence without green segment

In the following five pages is reproduced the sunset of Nov. 27, 1955, as an example of the pictures which were taken (at various seasons) of the first contact of the lower rim of the sun's disc with the 80 km distant sea horizon. Similarly the sinking of the last segment of the disc was recorded when the rays were passing through about the same layers of the atmosphere. In this series all photographs were taken on panchro-matic film, 1/200 sec. exposure with a focal length of 6 metres (compare also the sunset of the preceding day Nov. 26, 1955, on pp. 61, 95). The upper figure shows the beginning of the photo-graphs at M.E.T. 16h 41m 17s. The picture below is taken 7 sec. later. Note influence of fine layers of discontinuity in the atmosphere within this time inter-val. For the zenith distance and other notes see p. 99.

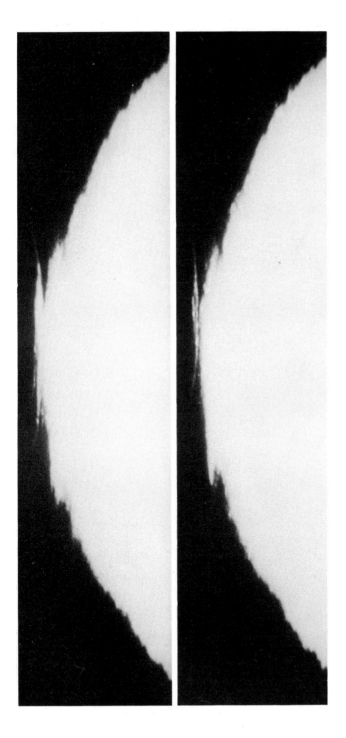

Continuation of the sunset of Nov. 27, 1955, on the preceding page: These two photographs of the upper rim were taken almost at the same time as those of the lower rim (cf page 85). Note the difference in the structure of the spikes. The upper photograph was taken at M.E.T. 16h 41m 45s, the lower photograph one second later. At the top, one can see distinctly the disappearing of a detached strip within one second. Note especially the tiny spikes of this strip with "upturned corners" and the influence of scintillation, which one can observe also on the green flash when it is very close to the horizon. The meteorological conditions of this sunset were good. It was sunny all day, without clouds and with no wind. Rel. humid. 55%, local temp. 3°C. The 80 km distant sea horizon was just visible, but above it there were distant layers of haze. Note the weather maps and radiosonde soundings on pp. 97, 98.

—h′
—h

Continuation of the sunset of Nov. 27, 1955, on the preceding page:
Upper picture: The 80 km distant sea horizon was lit up for the first time (h). There appeared a rare doubling of the luminous horizon line which however vanished rapidly (h′).

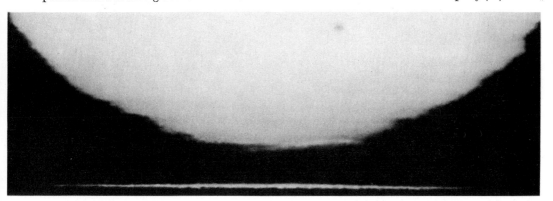

In the following pictures one can see progressively, almost second by second, the refraction and scintillation effects preceding the contact of the sun's rim with the distant sea horizon. Note also a sunspot and its variable form.

➡

Continuation of the preceding page: With some experience in observing this first
contact of the sun with a very distant sea horizon, one can estimate roughly how the
last rays will be affected by discontinuity layers or scintillation.

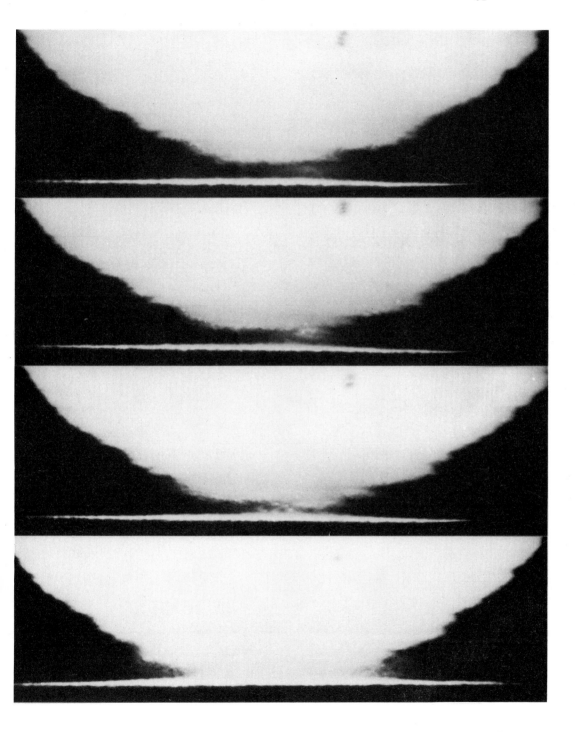

Continuation of sunset of Nov. 27, 1955, on the preceding page:
The top of the sun's disc passes through about the same atmospheric layers as the lower rim in the photographs on pp. 89, 91. The horizon line of the sea is still visible and very sharp in the three upper photos, but it has vanished in the following pictures in consequence of an apparent lifting of the last rays of the sun above the horizon (note similar effects in colour on pp. 77, 79). The last picture was a faint blue-green for about one second.

Chronograph-registered times of the photographs (from top to bottom): M.E.T. 16h 45m 49.1s — 16h 45m 51.2s — 16h 45m 56.0s — 16h 45m 57.1s — 16h 45m 58.7s. (The luminous horizon at the extreme edge at right of the pictures on page 91 was by chance somewhat curtailed by the film holder, which was not adjusted exactly parallel to the horizon. The extension of the luminous horizon was symmetrical, the left half is shown in its full length).

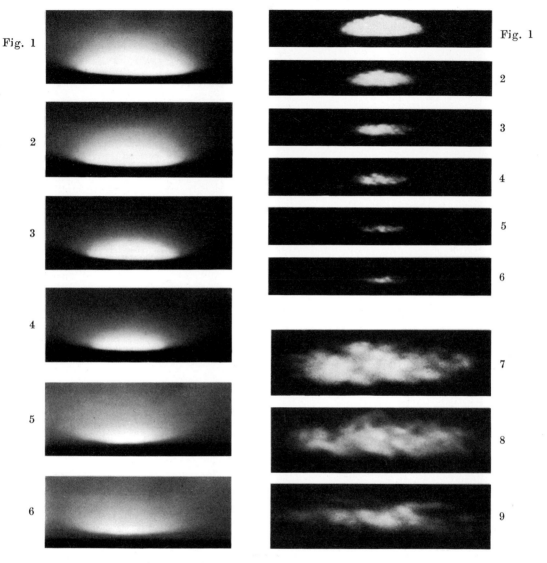

Two very different green flashes on the sea horizon
Taken with the 6 m refractor on Ektachrome

Oct. 7, 1955 — After this green flash disappeared (fig. 5), there remained a green glow with up-turned corners for about 5 seconds (fig. 6). Sun's diameter 5.5 cm. Distant seeing was good, but with strong, rapid, somewhat blurred scintillation (also on the horizon).

Nov. 26, 1955 — Fig. 1-6 are contact prints of the last segment (Sun's diameter 5.5 cm). There was a mere trace of a blue-green flash for about two seconds, very disturbed by flowing scintillation (fig. 7-9. Sun's diameter 20 cm).

See weather maps p. 97.

Radiosonde soundings Nov. 26, 1955

Local (Roma-Ciampino)						400 Km distant (Cagliari-Elmas)				
mb	m	°C	wind dir.	vel.		mb	m	°C	wind dir.	vel.
998	104	3,2	30°	25		1000	129	6,0	340°	11
939	600	1,0	20	36		916	850	0,8	360	18
880	1120	— 3,8	40	40		893	1070	— 0,4	10	19
850	1386	— 6,0	40	42	13	870	1270	— 1,4	360	20
808	1790	— 8,7	50	38	hours	850	1437	— 2,9	350	21
770	2160	— 8,9	50	30	before	810	1845	— 6,3	350	27
700	2882	—14,4	20	15	sunset	725	1980	— 6,6	350	28
632	3650	—20,8	280	16		700	2945	—14,1	340	33
587	4200	—22,8	340	16		670	3290	—15,7	340	36
500	5348	—29,5	10	27		660	3400	—15,2	350	36
						637	3680	—16,6	350	41
						600	4105	—17,7	350	51
						542	4870	—22,1	350	56
						534	4970	—22,3	350	56
						500	5449	—24,7	350	56
						1000	180	9,4	350	09
						870	1315	— 1,2	360	15
						850	1499	— 2,9	360	17
						820	1800	— 4,5	360	19
						795	2040	— 3,5	360	19
						787	2100	— 2,8	350	19
					3	771	2280	— 2,8	350	19
observations prevented					hours	758	2400	— 3,8	350	19
by strong wind					before	737	2640	— 4,3	350	19
					sunset	700	3026	— 7,0	350	24
						690	3140	— 7,0	350	25
						650	3610	— 9,0	350	28
						577	4505	—13,3	340	34
						542	4990	—15,6	340	32
						500	5590	—20,1	340	47

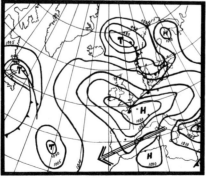

ARROW SHOWS DIRECTION OF SUNSET

9 hours before sunset

Radiosonde soundings Nov. 27, 1955

13 hours before sunset

\	Local (Roma-Ciampino)				\	400 Km distant (Cagliari-Elmas)			
mb	m	°C	wind dir.	vel.	mb	m	°C	wind dir.	vel.
1011	104	− 1,2	40°	12	1000	202	5,6	320°	05
1000	191	+ 1,0	40	10	850	1515	− 3,0	320	12
954	580	+ 2,3	60	07	710	2900	−12,5	320	20
850	1492	− 5,8	220	09	700	3019	−11,2	320	22
812	1870	− 8,6	290	04	680	3240	− 8,9	330	26
785	2140	− 6,0	30	11	500	5562	−24,2	330	45
700	3011	− 9,1	20	18					
690	3140	−10,3	20	17					
665	3420	−10,7	20	15					
620	3940	−13,9	40	11					
500	5535	−26,7	60	23					

3 hours before sunset

\	Local (Roma-Ciampino)				\	400 Km distant (Cagliari-Elmas)			
mb	m	°C	wind dir.	vel.	mb	m	°C	wind dir.	vel.
1013	104	8,8	00	00	1000	214	10,6	00	00
1000	210	6,9	00	00	850	1544	1,0	00	00
924	870	+ 0,6	260	06	797	2080	− 1,6	00	00
899	1090	+ 0,3	270	05	776	2290	− 0,3	350	14
880	1250	− 1,3	330	03	743	2620	− 0,8	10	10
871	1340	− 1,3	350	03	700	3094	− 2,5	10	17
850	1522	− 0,1	30	07	628	3910	− 7,2	10	19
841	1600	− 0,3	40	10	595	4320	−10,1	10	23
784	2170	− 2,4	30	09	562	4770	−11,3	10	25
744	2570	− 4,4	40	11	500	5659	−16,4	360	28
700	3055	− 6,1	30	17					
607	4160	−12,0	30	19					
598	4280	−12,1	30	21					
533	5140	−19,1	20	24					
500	5614	−23,0	10	27					

9 hours after sunset

\	Local (Roma-Ciampino)				\	400 Km distant (Cagliari-Elmas)			
mb	m	°C	wind dir.	vel.	mb	m	°C	wind dir.	vel.
1014	104	− 1,0	90	04	1020	85	8,0	00	00
1000	216	+ 3,5	80	04	1000	249	6,9	00	00
980	390	+ 3,5	60	03	904	1060	2,0	00	00
863	1400	+ 1,0	350	05	870	1380	+ 0,1	00	00
826	1770	+ 1,0	340	10	850	1568	− 0,3	330	06
766	2370	− 2,6	350	12	787	2180	− 2,0	330	04
746	2580	+ 1,9	10	15	726	2820	− 3,0	30	09
700	3073	− 4,6	10	16	700	3107	− 4,0	30	11
626	3950	−10,5	30	26	642	3680	− 8,2	20	15
575	4600	−14,8	30	23	592	4390	−13,8	10	17
557	4840	−17,1	20	27	586	4480	−13,8	10	18
500	5632	−21,5	20	25	500	5670	−22,0	10	22

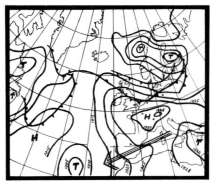

ARROW SHOWS DIRECTION OF SUNSET

9 hours before sunset

Sun's Zenith Distance at Sunsets over the Sea 1955-1957

Date	M.E.T. Sunset	Sun's Zenith Distance	Flash Dur. Form	Flash Col.	Sun col.	Sun Dist.	Haze	Scintill. Flash	Scintill. Hor.	Humid.	Wind	Temp.
1955	h m s	s								%		°C
Sept. 16	18 22 22	91°30'8	2*n	g	Y	d°	h'	ts'	z°s'	32	w'	14
» 19	18 17 16	91 32.2	2*n	g"-bg	Y	d"	h'	s'	z's°	60	w°	17
Nov. 11	16 57 40	91 32.0	2*n	g"-b"	YO	d°	h'	s'	z's°	85	w°	12
» 22	16 48 41	91 33.2	1*n	g'	YO	d'	h'	t"s'	z°s°	50	w°	6
» 23	16 48 07	91 33.8	1 n	g	OR	d'	h'	ts'	z's°	70	w°	5
» 27	16 45 59	91 33.9	1*n	bg	OR	d'	h'	s'	z's°	55	w°	3
Dec. 28	16 50 11	91 34.0	1*v	g'	Y	d'	h'	ts"	z°s°	40	w°	7
1956												
Jan. 11	17 02 36	91 41.5	1*	g	YO	d°	h'	s°	z'	75	w°	8
» 15	17 07 01	91 33.3	2	g	Y		h'	s'	z°s'	90	w'	9
Feb. 8	17 36 35	91 33.9	3n	g	OR	d°	h'	s"b	z's"	35	w'	-4
Mar. 6	18 09 28	91 33.8	3n	bg"-b"	Y	d°	h°	s°	z°s°	40	w°	6
» 26	18 31 59	91 33.6	2*vi	g	OR	d"	h'	s'	z°s°	85	w°	12
» 27	18 33 10	91 34.6	6*vi	g'-bg'	Y	d"	ch'	s'	z°s°	75	w°	10
Apr. 2	18 39 38	91 33.1	—		R	d°	h"	s°	z's°	70	w°	10
» 7	18 45 08	91 33.1	1*n	bg	OR		h'	s"	z's"	30	w'	0
» 8	18 46 13	91 32.9	1*n	g	OR	d°	h'	s"	z"s"	18	w'	0
» 9	18 47 22	91 33.5	1*n	bg	OR	d°	h'	s'	z"s'	55	w°	5
May 8	19 18 55	91 30.4	—		R	d°	h"	s'	z"s'	50	w°	15
Aug. 17	19 10 32	91 31.7		—	R	d°	h"		z"	50	w°	21
» 20	19 04 37	91 16.6		—	R	d°	h"	s'	z'	30	w°	25
» 24	18 59 50	91 31.8		—	R	d"	h"	ts"	z"s'	55	w°	20
» 30	18 50 33	91 36.3		—	OR	d"	h'	s'	z's°	50	w°	21
Sept. 8	18 35 10	91 33.8	1*n	g'	OR		h'	s'	z°s°	45	w°	19
» 15	18 22 51	91 31.5	1*n	bg'	YO	d"	h'	ts'	z's°	50	w°	21
» 16	18 21 07	91 31.5	1n	g	YO	d"	ch'	s°	z°s°	60	w°	21
» 17	18 19 19	91 32.4	2*n	bg	OR	d"	h'	t"	z's°	50	w°	20
» 18	18 17 39	91 32.1	1n	g	OR	d"	h'	s'	z's°	50	w°	20
» 30	17 56 56	91 32.5		—	R	d'	h'	s'	z's°	55	w°	19
Oct. 6	17 46 44	91 32.0	1n	1g	Y	d°	ch'	ts'	z°s°	35	w°	11
» 11	17 38 36	91 32.5	1ni	bg	OR	d'	h'	s°	z's°	45	w°	11
» 12	17 36 59	91 32.2	2n	bg	OR	d'	h'	ts'	z's'	45	w°	12
» 13	17 35 26	91 32.9		—	R	d'	h"	s"	z"s°	70	w°	12
» 14	17 33 48	91 32.4	1vi	bg	OR	d'	h'	s°	z's°	60	w°	11
» 16	17 30 43	91 32.8		—	R		h"		z'	65	w°	12
» 29	17 11 26	91 26.5	2*n	bg	OR		h'	s'	z' s'	60	w'	7
1957												
Jan. 7	16 59 28	91 34.6	1n	g	OR	d'	h'	s'	z's°	20	w'	
Mar. 2	18 04 24	91 32.5			R	d°	h"	s'	z"s'	20	w'	3
» 3	18 06 08	91 38.7	3n	bg	OR	d'	h'	t"s°	z's'	20	w°	6
» 4	18 06 48	91 33.1	3n	bg'	YO	d"	h'	t"s°	z's°	65	w°	7
» 5	18 08 08	91 34.9	2n	1g	Y	d'	h'	s'b	z°s°	80	w°	8
» 15	18 19 30	91 34.1		—	R	d"	h"	s°	z°s°	65	w°	9

In the above table are given also observations made visually by C. Treusch with the guiding telescope (1 m f.l.), with or without neutral filter (altitude 450 m, distance of sea horizon c 80 km). At times only approximate estimates were possible.

Col. 2 – M.E.T. of sunset (Middle European Time, 1 hour ahead of UT).
Col. 3 – **Zenith distance** of sun's centre, computed from the time in col. 2.

Col. 4 – **Duration of flash (in seconds):** * – denotes that the flash occurred above (pp. 3, 79), not on (pp. 73, 75, 129), the horizon. **Form of flash:** n – extension more horizontal than vertical (pp. 79, 93); v – extension more vertical than horizontal (p. 175); i – layered (pp. 57, 133).

Col. 5 – **Colour of flash:** lg – light green: g – emerald green; bg – blue-green; b – blue. Letters connected by hyphens indicate the time-sequence of colours in a flash. **Intensity of flash** is indicated by accents, for example: g – faint emerald green; g' – average intensity; g'' – intense (visible even through a neutral filter of average density).

Col. 6 – **Colour of sun** in the three minutes before sunset: Y – yellow to dark yellow; YO – yellow to orange; OR – orange to red; R – dark red.

Col. 7 – **Distortions of sun's disc:** d^o – slight flattening; d' – distortions with green strips; d'' – very marked distortions.

Col. 8 – **Haze:** h^o – none, or hardly any; h' – average; h'' – much haze. When the 80 km distant horizon is easily visible (z^o) and much haze is present (h''), then the latter lies beyond the horizon. c – indicates clouds very near the flash (p. 133).

Col. 9 – **Scintillation in flash** (or in last light, when no flash): s^o – none or hardly any; s' – average; s'' – very strong. t – signifies that the green disappeared less or more (t') coarse grained, steady (without the characteristic motion of scintillation). When the letters t and s are combined there was a mixture of the two types (it is hardly possible to distinguish one type from the other without a rapid sequence of exposures). f – signifies a flowing or flame-like scintillation in a preferred direction (pp. 59, 95); b – signifies that it was blurred.

Col. 10 – **Seeing** to the 80 km distant horizon: z^o – very good; z' – poor; z'' – horizon visible only in front of sun. s after z indicates the strength of the scintillation on the actual line of the horizon.

Col. 12 – **Wind, local:** w^o – calm; w' – light.

Col. 13 – **Local temperature** at sunset in °C. Note that the surface temperature of open water in the Tyrrhenian Sea usually does not fall below 13°-14°C in winter and does not exceed 24°-25°C in summer.

Note on Sunset of Aug. 7, 1956. The last tip of the sun remained in contact with the sea horizon for c. 35 seconds (C. TREUSCH). It remained to the last an intense red, with no trace of green or blue, in spite of excellent seeing. The change in refraction, as shown in the recordings of the sun's altitude (p. 151), was quite normal, so that the long delay was probably due to reflection.

Zenith Distance of the Sun at Sunset. The path of a light ray between observatory and horizon may be taken as approximately an arc of a circle with radius R/k, where R = earth's radius. If δR be the altitude of the observatory, d the dip of the horizon and a the elevation of the horizon due to refraction, then, with sufficient accuracy, $\sin d = \sqrt{2\delta(1-k)}$ and $\sin 2a = k\sqrt{2\delta/(1-k)}$. The following table gives d and a for our altitude (450 m) and various values of k:

k	.00	.10	.15	.20	.25	.30	.35	.40	.45	.50
d	40′.9	38′.8	37′.7	36′.6	35′.4	34′.2	33′.0	31′.7	30′.3	28′.9
a	0	2.1	3.3	4.5	5.9	7.3	8.8	10.5	12.4	14.5

$d + a$ changes very little for a considerable range in k or d; for $k = 0$ to $k = .30$ (twice the normal value), $d + a$ is about 41′. If z is the sun's zenith distance at sunset, r the horizontal astronomical refraction and s the sun's semi-diameter, then $z = 90° + d + a + r + s$. If $d + a = 41'$, $r = 35'$ (the usually adopted mean value) and $s = 16'$, then $z = 91°32'$. The mean value for the 41 sunsets in the table is 91°33′, so that the mean value of r here is 36′. The maximum observed value of z is 91°41′.5; r would then be about 44′.

COLTON[17] gives a list of zenith distances computed from the times of sunsets photographed by him at Lick. In some cases the resulting refraction is very great, over 2°. I have recomputed some of the zenith distances and obtain values more than 1° less than Colton's (e.g. on July 27, 1893, 92°44′.3 instead of 93°54′.5). This would make the refraction much less abnormal, although greater than any observed here.

C. The Green and the Red Flash,
Influenced by Layers of Discontinuity

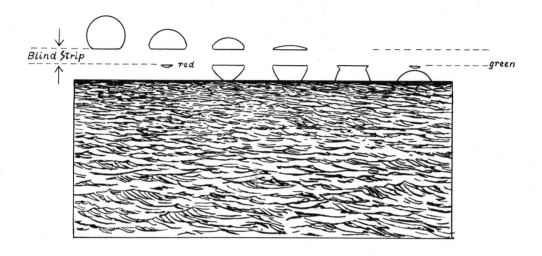

Part C begins with several sunset sequences in black-and-white, such as could be obtained with very simple instruments. It was thought worth while to devote some space to this, in order to show what can be done with quite modest means. Much useful information could be provided, for example, by photographing various details of a sunset (or sunrise) with several cameras in different positions (e.g. at different heights) with synchronised shutters. Such a study is not likely to be undertaken with the large telescopes of an observatory. In any case, many observatories are not suitably situated for such observations, or their telescopes do not reach down to the horizon. The field thus remains open to amateurs.

After these photographs, taken with comparatively short focal lengths, come some colour photographs taken with long focus telescopes, showing that the appearance of the sun's rim is affected by very distant atmospheric conditions. There follow details of sunsets that could be observed visually with quite small telescopes (and a neutral filter), but that can be photographed only with larger instruments.

The Green Flash on Four Successive Days
Sept. 15 – Sept. 18, 1956

These four sunsets (pp. 109-115) show particularly clearly the influence of discontinuities, " blind strips ", mirages. As far as possible the time sequence is indicated. A ROBOT camera with an objective of only 1 metre focal length was used; thus the green flash was so small that a good reproduction was not possible. It was thought better to describe the visual observations during each sunset. The time of appearance of the flash on each day is given in the table on page 99.

Many reproductions have been deliberately made so as to show a trace of sky background (with consequent loss of the much brighter fine details on the sun's rim). In this way it is possible to follow the influence of haze-layers, which are often also discontinuity layers, on the distortions of the sun's disc.

Two other interesting sunsets, but without a green flash, are shown immediately before the above series (Aug. 30 and Sept. 13). A summary of the general weather conditions in the general direction of sunset over this period (taken from the official weather maps) follows:

" For the first time for many months Central Europe is covered by a stable anticyclone of longer than about three days' duration. A steady state of this kind is quite common in the second half of September. Ordinarily it sets in about a week later, while about the middle of the month there comes the first cold breath of autumn."

Note the following weather maps and the radiosonde soundings on pp. 103, 178, 179.

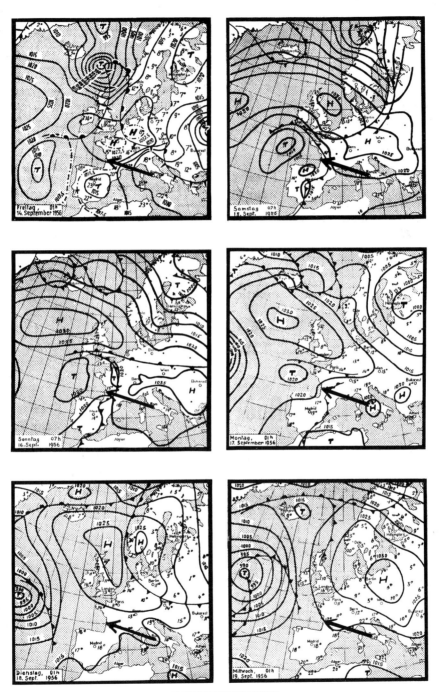

ARROW SHOWS DIRECTION OF SUNSET

➡

Aug. 30, 1956 – Sunset with red flash and high detached green strip. In the first picture (18h 45m 31s) the lower rim of the sun just touches a layer of discontinuity. Note how the rim is flattened. It remained for 20 seconds almost unchanged at a constant height above the horizon. Suddenly, in a fraction of a second, a red flash shot downwards, as seen in the photograph 18h 45m 52s. Its colour was a pure deep red for about one second. As this flash flowed into the rim of the sun the pure red gradually disappeared and the yellow colour of the sun predominated. Note a second red flash at 18h 46m 13s. At about the same height above the horizon as the first red flash there appeared an intense green detached strip on the upper portion of the sun's disc (18h 48m 52s). Other notes of this sunset on p. 102.

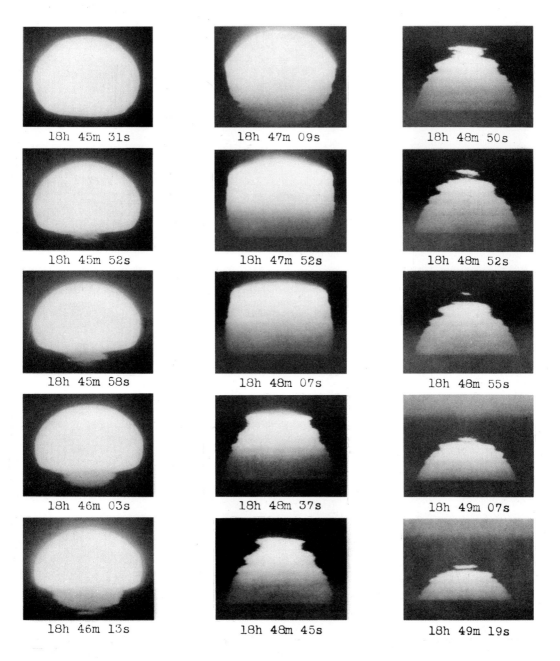

18h 45m 31s

18h 47m 09s

18h 48m 50s

18h 45m 52s

18h 47m 52s

18h 48m 52s

18h 45m 58s

18h 48m 07s

18h 48m 55s

18h 46m 03s

18h 48m 37s

18h 49m 07s

18h 46m 13s

18h 48m 45s

18h 49m 19s

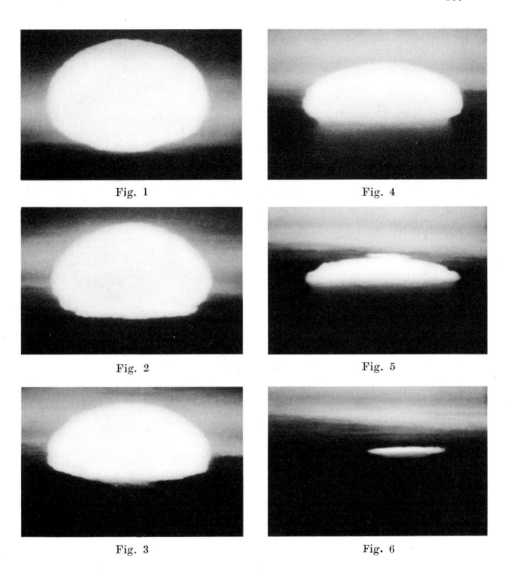

Fig. 1

Fig. 4

Fig. 2

Fig. 5

Fig. 3

Fig. 6

Sept. 13, 1956 – In this sunset, as in that of Aug. 30, the lower rim of the sun is touching a discontinuity layer, but the rim seems much more flattened (fig. 2). It remained longer at a constant height above the horizon, while the upper rim continued to move downwards (fig. 2 and 3). The consequence was a progressive vertical compression of the sun's disc as seen in the pictures. There was perhaps a trace of a red flash below the intense yellow sun (fig. 3), weakened probably by thick haze in the layer of discontinuity. At about the same height as this flattened rim the upper portion of the sun's disc vanished with a faint red-coloured detached strip, without any green (fig. 6). Other notes on p. 102.

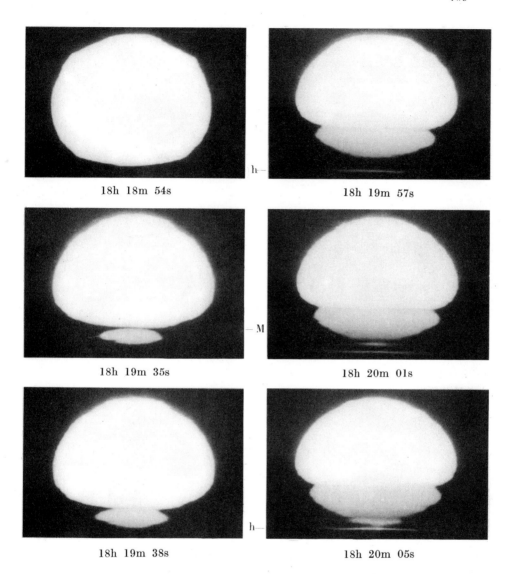

18h 18m 54s

18h 19m 57s

18h 19m 35s

18h 20m 01s

18h 19m 38s

18h 20m 05s

Sept. 15, 1956 – This is the first of four successive sunsets with the green flash. After a drop of temperature " nearly everywhere ", as noted in the Bollettino Meteorologico, a period of fine weather commenced. It was sunny all day, with no wind. Note in these photographs the characteristic distortions of the sun's disc, caused evidently by a marked vertical difference in temperature. There was an interesting " blind strip " (M) as seen beginning with the picture at 18h 19m 35s. Note its influence on the sun's rim as the latter moved downwards. In the 18h 20m 01s photograph one can observe a small red flash completely separated from the sun's rim and very close to the luminous sea horizon, where a green flash appeared some three minutes later. For the time of appearance and other notes see pp. 99, 102, 103.

➡

Sept. 16, 1956 – Continuation of the four day period of sunsets. The weather conditions were almost unchanged. It was clear all day with no wind, only some clouds
in the direction of sunset. In the pictures 18h 17m 22s – 28s one can observe the
presence of a discontinuity layer, as in the preceding sequence (Sept. 15), and also
a " blind strip ". The distant clouds had no observable influence on the sun's rim.
Where the " blind strip " appeared, a high and intense green detached strip was
formed at 18h 20m 13s. On the horizon h there was a distinct but rather faint green
flash. For the time and other notes see pp. 99, 102, 103.

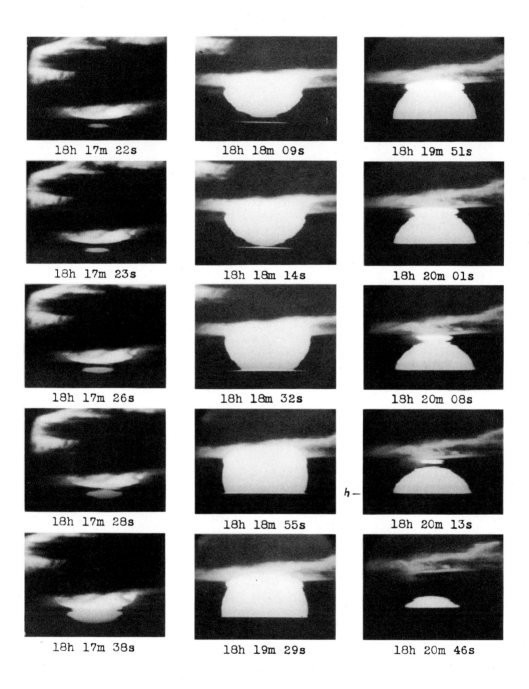

18h 17m 22s   18h 18m 09s   18h 19m 51s

18h 17m 23s   18h 18m 14s   18h 20m 01s

18h 17m 26s   18h 18m 32s   18h 20m 08s

18h 17m 28s   18h 18m 55s   18h 20m 13s

18h 17m 38s   18h 19m 29s   18h 20m 46s

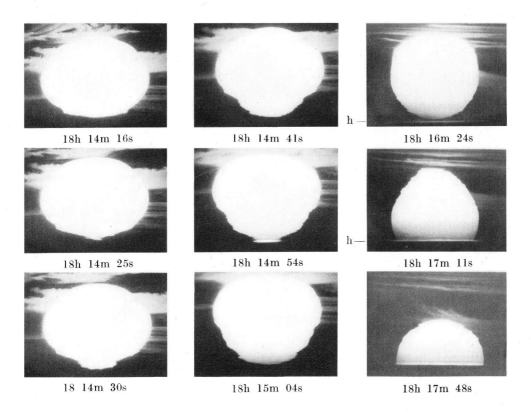

18h 14m 16s

18h 14m 41s

h — 18h 16m 24s

18h 14m 25s

18h 14m 54s

h— 18h 17m 11s

18 14m 30s

18h 15m 04s

18h 17m 48s

Sept. 17, 1956 – Continuation of the four day period of sunsets. The characteristic
" blind strip " of the two preceding sunsets seems to have now vanished but there
was a marked vertical elongation of the sun's disc as seen in the photograph 18h
17m 11s. All day was sunny with no wind, but there were some high layers of haze
which for a long time (45 minutes) after sunset were still almost white. There was a
blue-green flash. For the time and other notes see pp. 99, 102, 103.

Sept. 18, 1956 – The " blind strip " of the sunsets of Sept. 15 and Sept. 16 has reappeared (M). The weather conditions were still good. In these photographs there is a slight haze in discontinuity layers, which can be followed in many pictures at d. Note in the last photographs (18h 17m 01s) the extremely high detached strip which vanished with an intense emerald green. There was a faint green flash on the very sharp horizon h for one second. For time and other notes see pp. 99, 102, 103. (The dark shadows in the lower corners of some pictures are caused by the frame of the ROBOT camera. They are absent when the sun's disc is exactly centred).

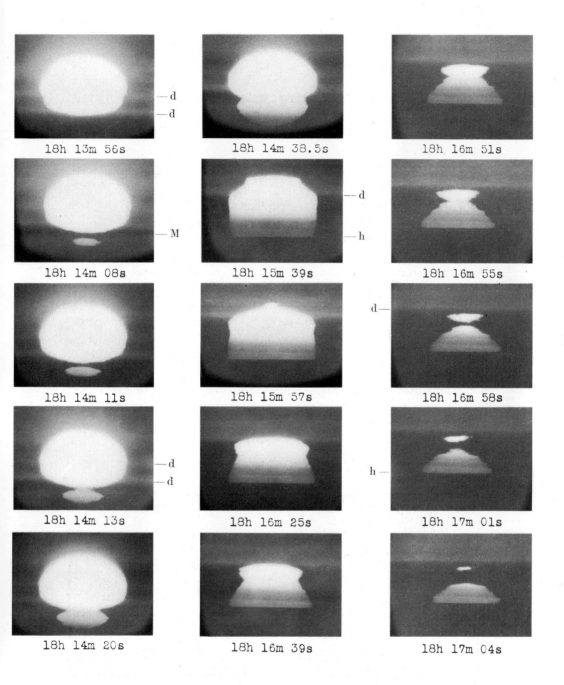

18h 13m 56s   —d
               —d

18h 14m 38.5s

18h 16m 51s

18h 14m 08s   — M

18h 15m 39s   —d
               —h

18h 16m 55s

18h 14m 11s

18h 15m 57s

d—

18h 16m 58s

18h 14m 13s   —d
               —d

18h 16m 25s

h —

18h 17m 01s

18h 14m 20s

18h 16m 39s

18h 17m 04s

116

Sunset with Green Flash Dec. 28, 1955
Reproduced in colour on page 3 (Plate I)

With yellow sunsets there is a much better chance of an interesting green or blue-green flash, as on this evening in midwinter, with no wind, temperature without any remarkable variations since the previous day, 40 % rel. humidity, 7°C local temp. Clear everywhere to a great distance, but very high strips of haze. Sun's rim in telescope almost without scintillation. This last note seems important because the photographs give a contrary impression of a very disturbed, coarse-grained, blurred scintillation which was in fact absent. It was more like a very slow turbulent motion, as in a fresh mixture of two liquids with different refractive indices, placed in the path of a light beam on an optical bench. The same very slow motion appeared in the ragged green flash which vanished at M.E.T. 16^h 50^m 11^s, after about 1 sec. as a pure emerald green. Less than twenty hours later a period of bad weather began, with cloud and rain, but no local wind. See also radiosonde soundings, p. 177, and table of sun's zenith distance, p. 99.

The bottom picture showing a ship about 80 km away was taken two hours before sunset with several different exposure times. The rough sea near the horizon sparkled brightly. None of the exposures showed any trace of green colour effect at the borders of the reflections in individual waves.

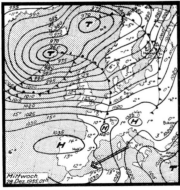

ARROW SHOWS DIRECTION OF SUNSET

16 hours before sunset

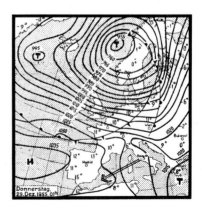

8 hours after sunset

Sunset with Green and Blue Flash Aug. 13, 1954
Reproduced in colour pp. 119-129

First successful series of colour photographs, taken with Leica camera in the Newtonian focus of the reflector, f.l. 2.4 m, stopped down to about 10 cm, beginning with 1/1000 sec. exposure time. Film: Ferraniacolor Invertibile.

Meteorological notes: Very good seeing to the 80 km distant sea horizon. Almost no scintillation. No local wind. 25% rel. humidity. 21°C local temp. See also radiosonde soundings, p. 176.

Sun setting behind the horizon an intense yellow to orange. Sixteen minutes before sunset tiny red flashes began to appear on the lower rim of the sun in quick succession (within a few seconds of each other) and some three minutes later tiny green detached strips on the upper rim, with about the same rhythm, evidently caused by fine layers of discontinuity. Eight minutes before sunset the sun was still an intense white yellow. Two minutes later the sun's disc was compressed over a discontinuity layer and changed colour to a darker yellow, at which moment the sequence of photographs began (p. 119). After sunset there was no trace of a red after-glow. Towards the next morning the setting moon (nearly at the full) was observed with interest, in order to see how it would appear when passing through the fine layers of discontinuity that were noticed on the previous sunset. The following notes were made:

Twenty minutes before the moon reached the sea horizon it had a distinct green and red rim in the guiding telescope (f.l. 1 m). Some time later tiny faint green detached strips were observed, similar to those seen on the upper rim of the sun ten hours before. The good seeing changed rapidly before sunrise, due to a light SE wind with 30% rel. humid., 21°C local temp. It remained dry all next day, but distant seeing was bad.

➡

Upper fig. – The lower rim of the sun, near a discontinuity layer, becomes more and more flattened.

Lower fig. – A red flash appeared suddenly. The photograph, reproduced here, was taken about one second later.

Plate XV 119

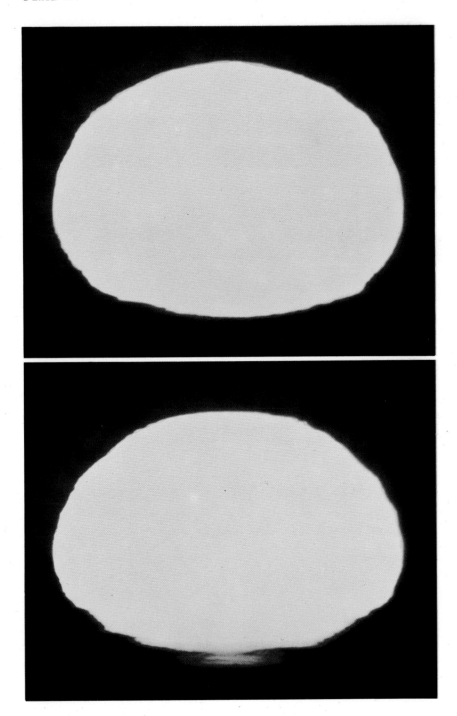

➡

Upper fig. – Note for the first time the appearance of the sea-horizon h, a very dark red line at the bottom of the picture.

Lower fig. – Another red flash appears, this time completely separated from the sun for about one second, glowing with an intense purple light.

Plate XVI   121

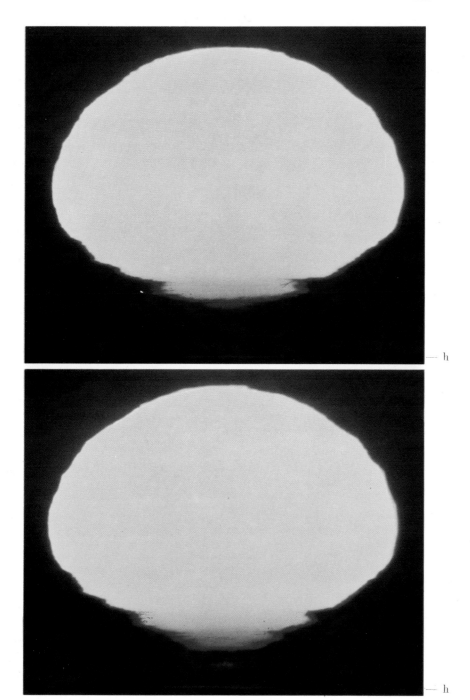

— h

— h

➡

As the lower portion of the sun's disc enters the discontinuity layers, it is gradually elongated. The upper portion of the sun, above the layers, remains still compressed. There is formed the well known Ω form of the setting sun, but in this case with a very definite separation of the red and green rim.

PLATE XVII

123

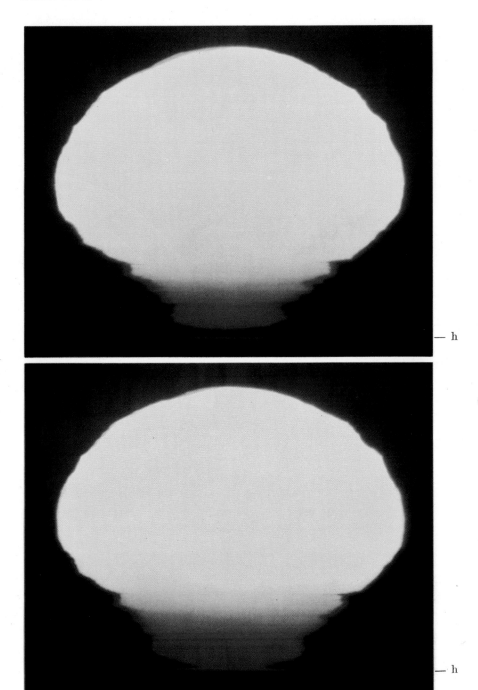

— h

— h

Continuation of sequence on preceding page. ➡

Plate XVIII   125

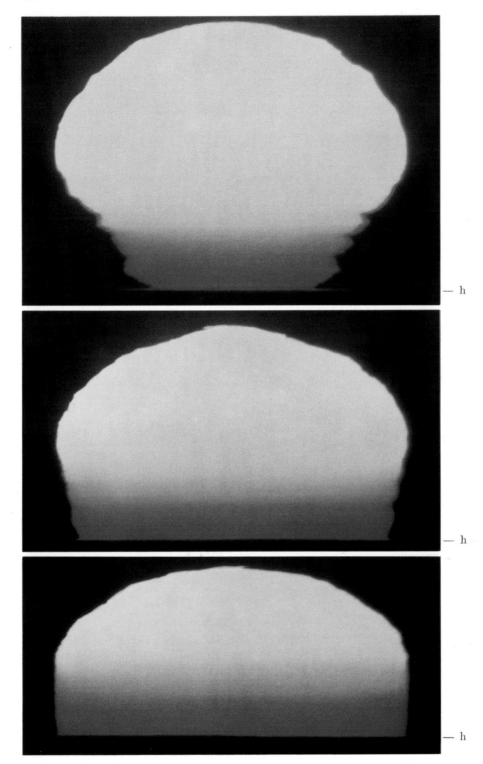

— h

— h

— h

➡

Note the deep notches in the sun's image, indicating several layers of discontinuity. By an unusual chance it was possible to catch a ship on the horizon. It was about 80 km distant. Details of its rigging can be seen on the 35 mm original film.

PLATE XIX 127

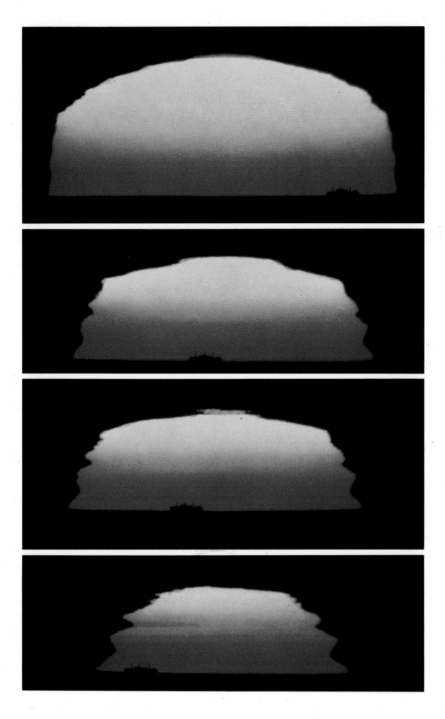

PLATE XX   129

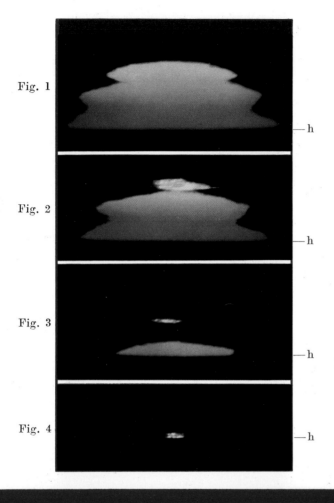

Fig. 1

—h

Fig. 2

—h

Fig. 3

—h

Fig. 4

—h

Fig. 5

—h

Some seconds before sunset other strips begin to be cut off, disappearing with a brilliant pure emerald-green, sometimes remaining afloat as if they were suspended freely in space. The visual colour of the last flash of sunlight changed rapidly from emerald-green to a blue-green mixture to blue. Fig. 4 was taken about half a second before the colour turned to pure blue. Compare it with the black-and-white magnification (fig. 5) and note the direct contact with the horizon at *h*. Note also how much sharper is the image of the ship (plate XIX) than the flash, taken exactly in the same focus.

Influence of Several Discontinuity Layers on a Green Flash

Photographs on the following pages 133, 135

Sunset March 27, 1956 – One of the most interesting green flashes of the past two years, after a long period of bad weather. Very seldom had the influence of so many discontinuity layers, one above the other, been observed in the green flash. At the last moment it turned more blue-green (bottom picture). The sun was a dark yellow until the emerald green appeared (upper picture). When touching the sea the lower portion of the sun's disc formed a pillar about as wide as the green flash which appeared later (p. 135). Some distant clouds partly covered the lower section of the flash. Note the luminous line on the horizon below this cloud, sometimes broken just where the cloud is higher.

The seeing was good as far as the 80 km distant sea horizon, but further off there was some high haze in front of the sun. At sunset no wind, very little scintillation, 75% rel. humidity, 10°C local temperature. Photographs taken with the 6 metre refractor on Ektachrome (under-exposed). Sun's diameter 21 cm on page 133.

Chronograph-registered times (p. 133):
M.E.T. 18h 33m 3.8s 18h 33 6.3s 18h 33 8.3s 18h 33m 10s (bottom picture).

It is interesting to compare this time (18h 33m 10s) with the time when the green flash of the preceding day vanished (p. 99) in a similar, but less striking, form.

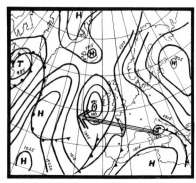

ARROW SHOWS DIRECTION OF SUNSET

11 hours before sunset

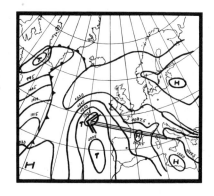

11 hours after sunset

Fig. 1

Fig. 2

Continuation of sunset March 27, 1956 on preceding page

Fig. 1 - Note the strange pillar formed when the lower rim is in contact with the very sharp 80 km distant sea horizon h. Sun's diameter 21 cm.

Fig. 2 shows clearly the influence of the same layers of discontinuity on the upper and lower rim of the sun within an interval of about 2.5 min. Fig. 1 was cut in two (at T) and the two halves (A and B) are mounted right and left of the green flash F, at the same altitude above the horizon h. Note how some distortions of the green flash and of the lower rim of the sun fit approximately into one another.

Comparison of the upper and lower rim of the sun on the horizon.   ➡

Dec. 8, 1955 – In this sunset are mounted together some exposures which contras-
ted visually in colour with the preceding sequence. The influence of thin layers of
discontinuity was also strong but there was no trace of a green flash. The setting sun
was an intense red, without noticeable scintillation, on a sharp 80 km distant sea
horizon. Note the thin " blind strip " (M1-M4) always at a constant height above
the horizon h. Note how the upper and lower rim fit approximately into each other
in the more highly magnified bottom picture (the make up is explained on p. 135).
    All photographs were taken with the 6 metre refractor on Ektachrome.

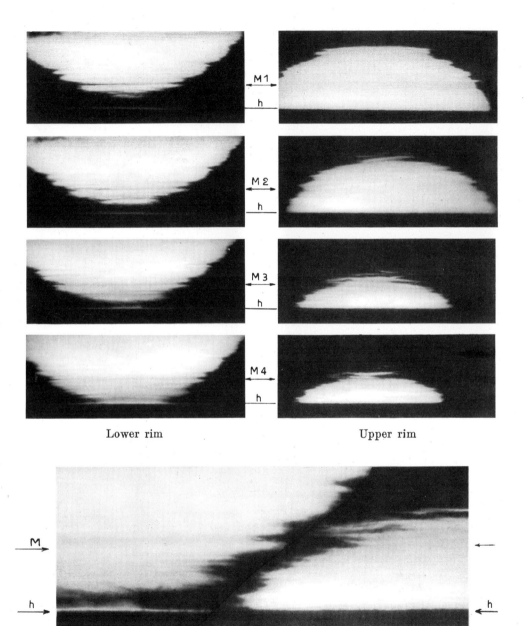

Lower rim   Upper rim

10

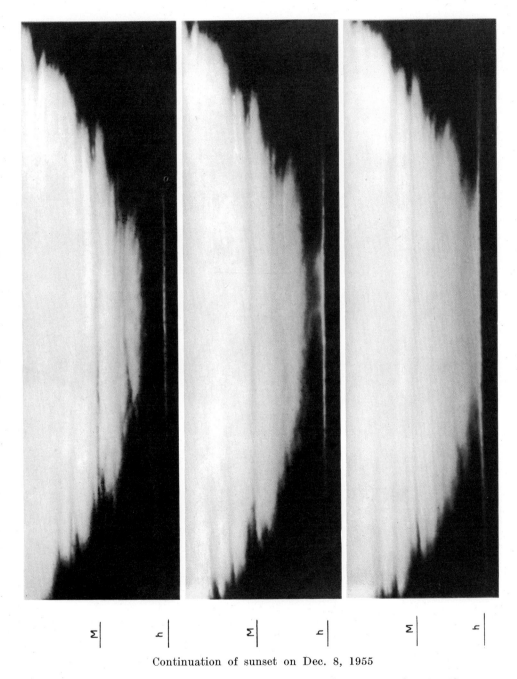

Continuation of sunset on Dec. 8, 1955

The sun is touching the sea horizon. The photos are the same as those on the preceding page, in which the upper and the lower rim are compared, but more highly magnified in order to show fine details on the sun's rim. Sun's diameter 21 cm.

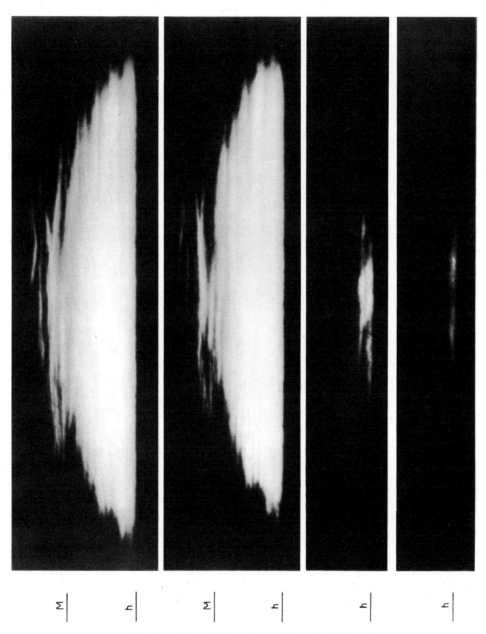

Continuation of sunset on Dec. 8. 1955

The last segment of the sun's disc vanished without a green flash. By holding over the pictures a scale perpendicular to the horizon one can easily follow the influence on this last segment of some of the fine layers of discontinuity of the preceding sequence (p. 139). The times were not registered. Sun's diameter 21 cm.

Green and red flash near high discontinuity layers.　　　　➡

Upper figure: Mar. 25, 1955 – Red flash about 1º above sea horizon, taken with 60 cm reflector (f. l. 2.4 m) stopped down to about 20 cm. Exposure 1/200 sec. with Leica-camera on Kodachrome daylight. Some haze near (invisible) horizon, no wind and no cloud, rel. humid. 85%.

Lower figure: July 6, 1954 – Green flash near high discontinuity layer, very disturbed by slow coarse-grained scintillation, whereas the horizon (90 km distant Tolfa Moun-tains) was so sharp that one can see individual trees in the original filmstrip. Taken as the preceding photograph, but with 1/60 sec. exposure, with Leica-camera.

PLATE XXI   143

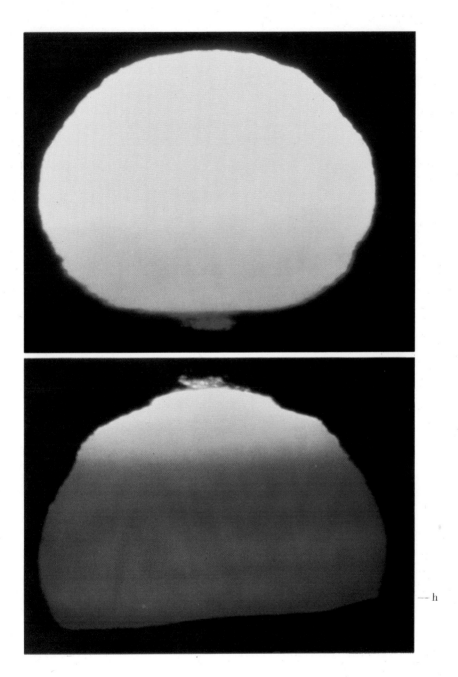

—h

Appendix

	Page
Technical equipment and registrations	146-152
Experiments with artificial discontinuity layers . . .	153-160, 165
Comparison of artificial and actual sunsets	156, 160-161
Various scintillation effects (highly magnified)	161-163, 167-171
Examples of colour effects on incorrectly exposed photographs of the green flash etc.	173-175
Weather maps and radiosonde soundings for the sunsets in Parts B and C	176-179

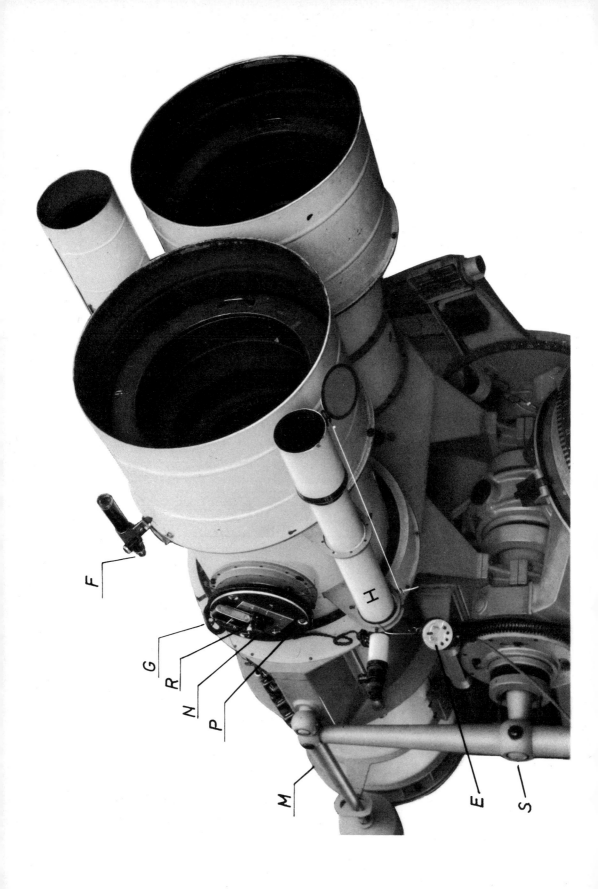

ASTROGRAPH IN HORIZONTAL POSITION, POINTING SOUTH

(when pointing west the two tubes are vertically one over the other). The camera equipment for photographing the green flash is mounted provisionally in the Newtonian focus.

F) Finder with neutral filter and crosswires, f.l. 30 cm.

H) Ditto with f.l. 1 metre

M) Mirror, aperture 60 cm, f.l. 2.4 metre

S) Declination axis

P) Plate with:

N) Leica Sliding Attachment

G) Focusing wheel

E) Electric switches for R.A and Dec. motions of the astrograph

R) Leica or Reflex camera

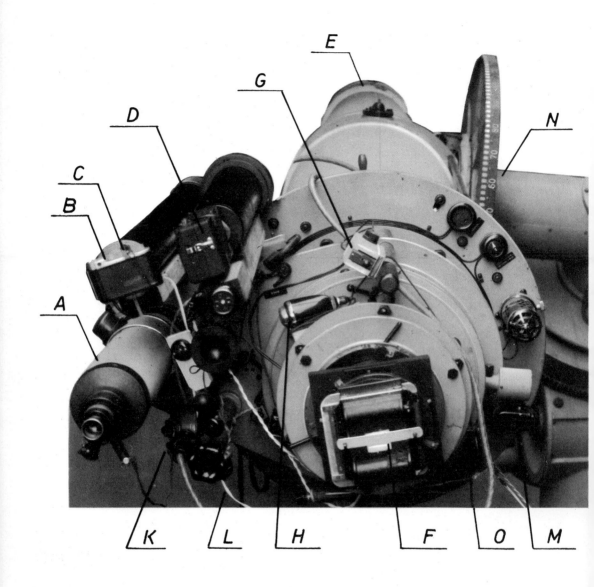

ZEISS 6 METRE REFRACTOR IN HORIZONTAL POSITION

A) Finder with neutral filter and cross wires.

B) ROBOT camera for several exposures a second, format 24×24 mm. The film transport mechanism is wound up after 15-20 exposures. Focal length of the MERZ objective $= 1$ metre (from a transit-instrument).

C) Electrical contact for the chronograph, synchronised with the camera shutter. Only a few seconds are required to move the ROBOT camera to the focus of the refractor at F.

D) Motion-picture 16 mm film-camera (Bell and Howell Co.). The camera operates at different speeds with an electric motor. KODAK metal magazines permit a quick change from black-and-white to colour film, which is of great importance in the very short interval, often only a few seconds, just before the last rays of the setting sun. Strips of 16 mm colour-film, one metre long and less, for tests of exposure times, can be inserted in a special magazine for immediate processing. This camera, like the ROBOT, can be inserted in the focus of the 6 metre refractor at F, in order to get cinematographic exposures of details of the gradual disappearance of small green flashes, when sufficiently bright. Instead of the 16 mm camera a light-weight 35 mm film-camera can be attached.

E) Tube of the refractor in horizontal position with Zeiss E-objective, aperture 400 mm, f.l. 6 metre.

F) Film-holder for E 120 roll-film (6×9 cm pictures). Immediately in front of the holder is a shutter, synchronised with the chronograph. This 6×9 cm frame can be quickly reduced by means of masks to about 2×6 cm and less, allowing the number of exposures to be more than tripled for a normal E 120 roll-film.

G) Electrical contact for indicating the altitude of the sun during a series of exposures (and in exact time intervals, see page 150).

H) Microphone of a tape-recorder. The recorder is set to work at the same time as the chronograph. In addition to the observations spoken into it, it records as noises the sound of second and minute contacts of the master clock, the operating time of the 16 mm or 35 mm moving film camera, the easily audible working of the ROBOT camera and the shutter on the 6 metre refractor.

K) Electric switches for the RA and Dec. slow motions of the refractor.

M) Motor (focusing).

N) Declination axis of the refractor.

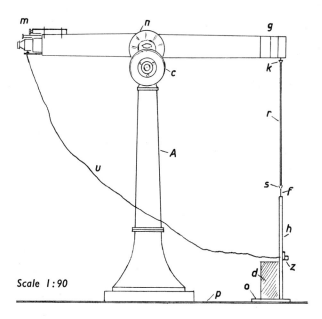

Scale 1 : 90

Improvised arrangement sometimes used for registering quickly, and with sufficient accuracy, the altitude of the sun's upper rim above the horizon on strips of chronograph paper, at intervals of 15 seconds. The strips provide immediately, without complicated calculations, a clear picture of the change in the refraction from about 20 minutes before sunset up to the moment in which the green flash appears (for examples of these registration strips see p. 151).

A still simpler method had been used previously. The image of the sun was projected through a pinhole, as in a camera obscura, on the light-coloured wall of the dome (or on a transparent screen 7 metres from the aperture) and the position of the sun's upper rim was marked every 15 seconds. This series of marks, which of course follows the line of the ecliptic, enables one to follow easily the changes in the refraction.

A) 6 metre refractor.

m) Eyepiece.

n) Declination circle.

C) Counterweight in RA.

g) Tube near objective.

z) Electric registration.

u) Circuit (z to m).

k) Cardan joint.

r) Thin-walled steel tube.

s) Another Cardan joint.

f) Flat bar in a sliding guide.

h) Sliding guide.

d) Base, loaded with lead.

o) Metal plate.

p) Floor of dome.

The tube r will naturally shift slightly from the vertical position. Within certain limits allowance can easily be made for this effect.

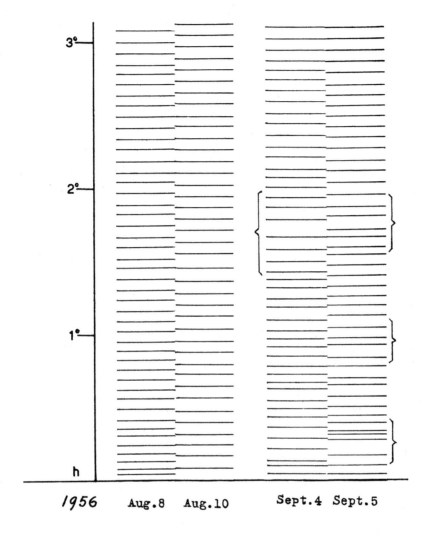

1956   Aug.8   Aug.10   Sept.4 Sept.5

Recording Strips, Showing the Influence of Discontinuity Layers at Sunset
over the Sea (made with the apparatus described on p. 150)

During the recording the upper rim of the sun was kept on the cross-
wires by means of the drive of the 6 m refractor and the electric slow motion
in declination. Every 15 seconds an electric circuit was closed, causing a
mark to be made on the vertical recording strip under the objective. Note
the vertical oscillations of the sun's upper rim, which are clearly shown by
the varying separation of the lines as the sun nears the horizon *h*. Similar
variations can be seen in the upper portions of the recordings, although
the differences here are much less and the lines appear at first glance to be
equidistant (an example of this as recorded on the chronograph can be seen
on p. 152).

152

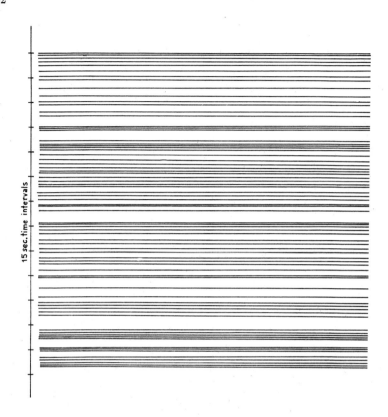

15 sec. time intervals

Fine Layers of Discontinuity on Bright Yellow Sun
(recorded 16 minutes before sunset, April 17, 1955)

Each horizontal line corresponds to a contact on the chronograph at the instant in which a tiny detached shred parted from the sun's upper rim with a blue-green flash. An example of a detachment of this kind can be seen (highly magnified) in the cinematograph pictures on p. 162. The distance between the lines of the recording shows thus the rhythm in which these tiny flashes occur. If one places such a sequence of lines over a (correspondingly magnified) photograph of the upper third of the sun's disc, taken at the start of the recording, it can be seen that the distance between many of the fine spikes on the sun's rim reproduce approximately the rhythm of the chronograph recording of the detached strips. A similar phenomenon was observed in the oscillations of the Venus trail (p. 67) and in the small vertical oscillations of sunspots (the height above the horizon has a marked influence on the extent of the oscillations).

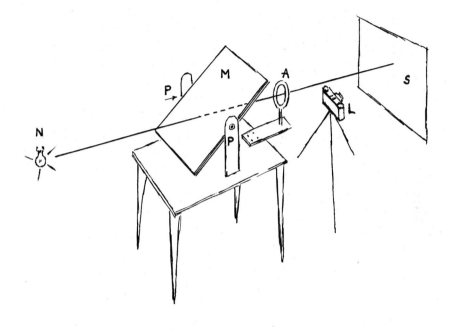

SKETCH OF IMPROVISED APPARATUS USED IN THE FOLLOWING PICTURES FOR PHOTOGRAPHING ARTIFICIAL FINE LAYERS OF DISCONTINUITY

The light of a distant 200 watt lamp N passed through three panes of window glass M, each about 1.5 mm thick, fixed together with scotch tape. The shadows of the discontinuity streaks in the glass plates, cast by the light, fell on a white screen S and were photographed with the Leica L placed somewhat lower. Photographs of the shadows were taken for various inclinations to the horizontal of the glass plates M (movable around the PP axis).

Note the effect of this angle in the pictures on p. 154.

Note the silhouette of the cardboard ring A (p. 155), of about 9 cm diameter, as it passes through the streaks (p. 154) with effects similar to those on the upper and lower rim of the setting sun near layers of discontinuity.

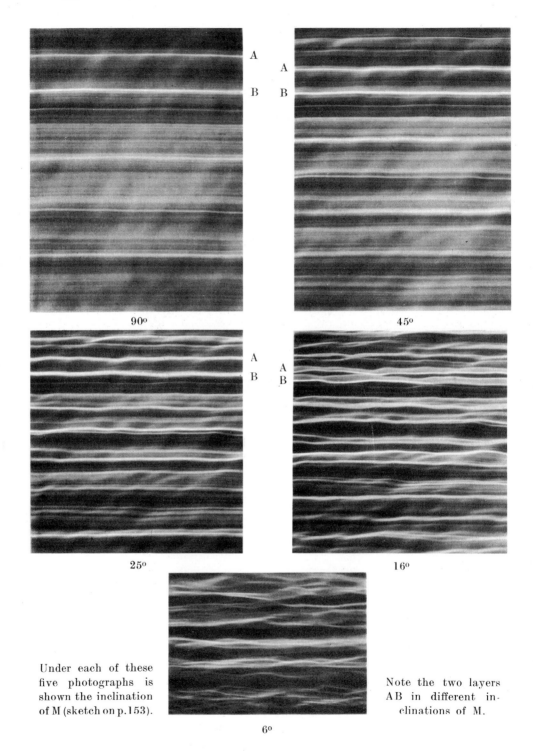

90°

45°

25°

16°

6°

A
B

A
B

A
B

A
B

Under each of these five photographs is shown the inclination of M (sketch on p.153).

Note the two layers AB in different inclinations of M.

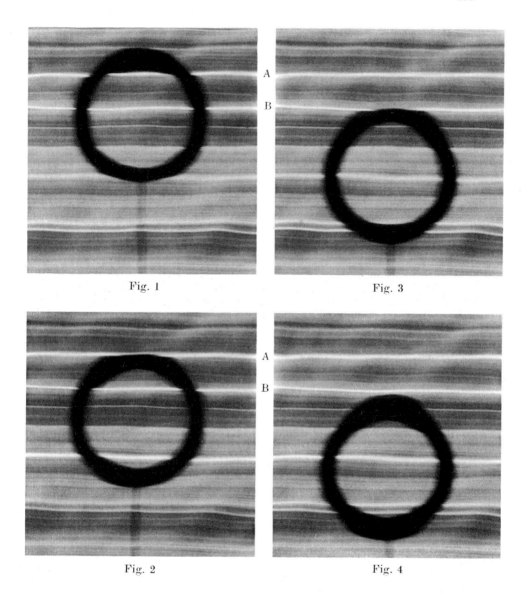

Fig. 1

Fig. 3

Fig. 2

Fig. 4

Ring moving as rising sun

In all the pictures one can observe effects similar to those in actual sunsets. In fig. 2 note the flattened upper rim near discontinuity layer A and its "shooting up" in figure 1.

Ring moving as setting sun

In fig. 3 the upper rim is just passing the discontinuity layer B in the opposite direction to the motion in figs. 1 and 2.
In fig. 4 one has the impression that the rim sticks for a moment to B, as opposed to the "shooting up".

156

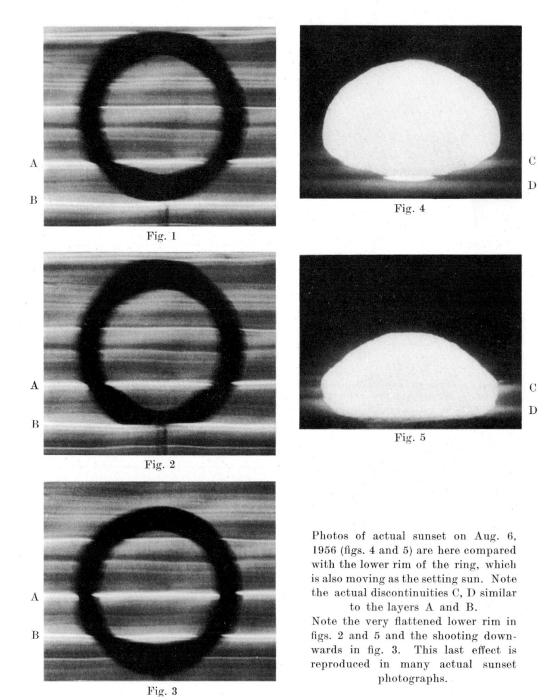

Fig. 1

Fig. 4

A

B

Fig. 2

A

B

C

D

C

D

Fig. 5

A

B

Fig. 3

Photos of actual sunset on Aug. 6, 1956 (figs. 4 and 5) are here compared with the lower rim of the ring, which is also moving as the setting sun. Note the actual discontinuities C, D similar to the layers A and B.

Note the very flattened lower rim in figs. 2 and 5 and the shooting downwards in fig. 3. This last effect is reproduced in many actual sunset photographs.

Upper and lower rim of a cardboard disc (moving from 1 to 6 as the setting sun) near two layers of discontinuity. Compare the effects of A and B (the same layers as on pp. 154-156) on the upper and lower rim. These pictures resemble some actual sunsets and also Scheiner's drawings (p. 180).

158

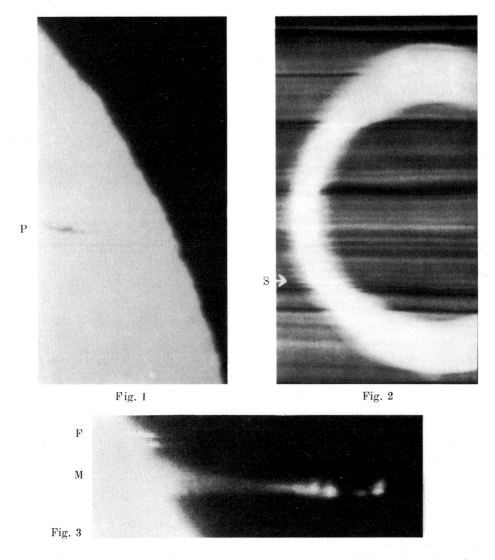

P

S →

F

M

Fig. 1

Fig. 2

Fig. 3

In fig. 2 note the many thin spikes (S) corresponding to the series of thin layers of discontinuity (experiment p. 153). In actual sunsets these layers are invisible against the sky background, but one can see their effects as very fine spikes. This appears in the highly magnified photograph of part of the sun's disc (fig. 3) taken about 15 min. before sunset with the 6 metre refractor (sun's diameter 105 cm). At F on the rim are two very fine spikes. They wandered, with many others, apparently upwards and gave rise to tiny blue detached strips. Fig. 1 shows a distant 4-engine plane (P) that chanced to pass across the sun. At M (fig. 3) is seen a diffuse trail left by the plane. The turbulent light effects in this trail (reflections?), as bright as the sun itself, disappeared almost instantaneously while the nearby spikes (F) remained.

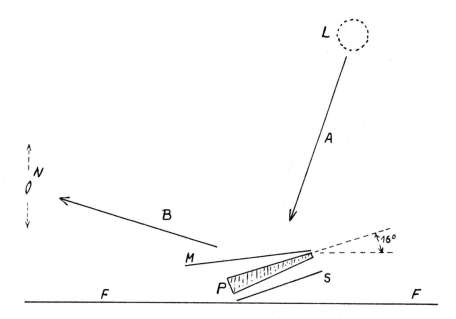

APPARATUS USED FOR COLOUR PHOTOGRAPHS OF ARTIFICIAL SUNSETS WITH RED AND GREEN FLASHES

In the similar experiment on p. 153 (without prism) no colour effects were obtained.

L Artificial sun (spherical ceiling lamp of opal glass with 100 w. lamp).

M Three glass plates, inclined 6° to the horizontal.

P 8° objective prism, 60 cm diameter, inclined 16° to the horizontal, as shown in sketch (it is of course not necessary to use so large a prism).

S Mirror.

F Floor.

N Cine-camera, movable vertically as shown by arrows.

A Incident ray.

B Reflected ray.

160

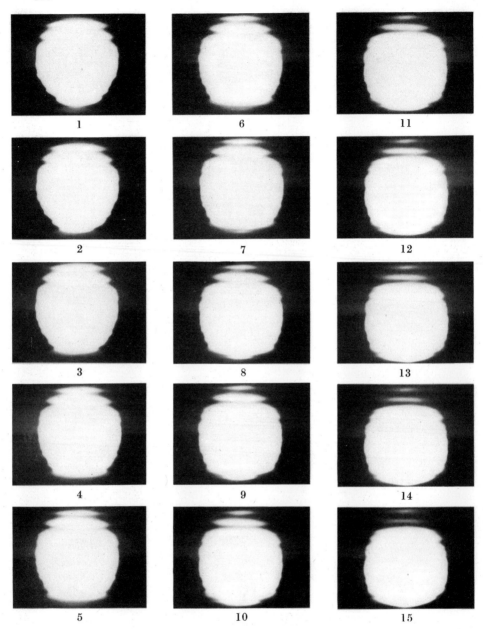

Artificial sunset sequence taken with the arrangement described on the preceding page, exposed on Ektachrome 135 (for artificial light). The cine-camera at N
was moved a few mm downwards after each exposure (while the artificial sun
remained fixed). Note the effect when the artificial solar disc is passing the discontinuity-layers in the same three glass plates, as shown on p. 153. The detached
strips finished (pictures 14 and 15) with a pure blue or blue-green, but never
emerald green.

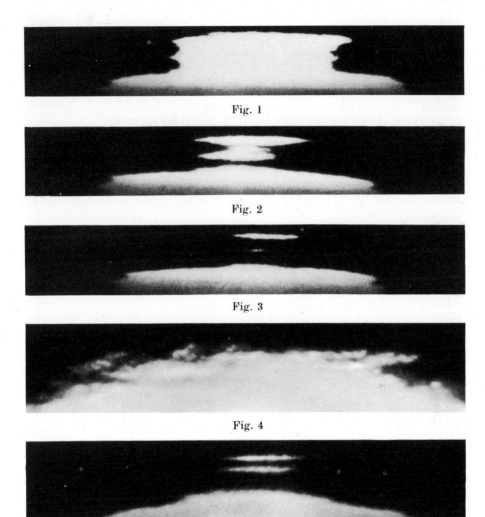

Fig. 1

Fig. 2

Fig. 3

Fig. 4

Fig. 5

Detached strips on the upper rim during actual sunsets, caused by several layers of discontinuity. They permit a comparison between the behaviour of actual and artificial discontinuity-layers, showing also the effects of scintillation. (Sun's diameter about 38 cm).

Fig. 1-3 - Sunset Aug. 31, 1954. Deep red detached strips very near the horizon during a red sunset.
Fig. 4 - Sunset Nov. 27, 1955. Note influence of strong scintillation.
Fig. 5 - Sunset Sept. 17, 1954. These two strips, which floated for about two seconds near the horizon, were a brilliant blue-green; a third was too faint to show in the reproduction.

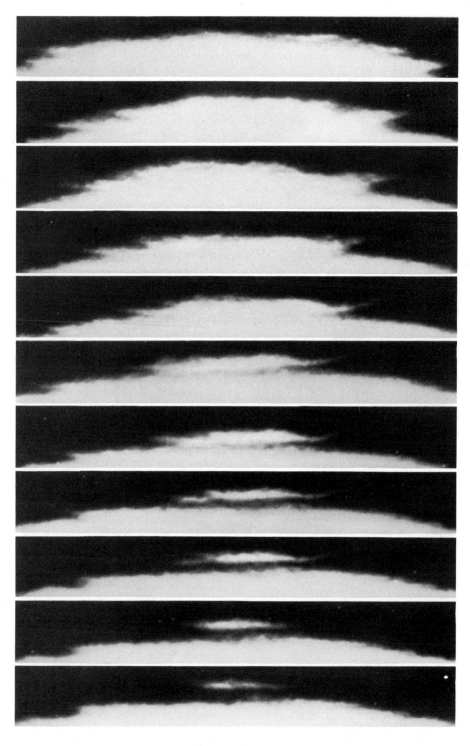

Development of a green detached strip with upturned corners (p. 162), c. 4 pictures per second. Scintillation effects (p. 163), three sequences in one sunset (all 1/200 sec. exposures).

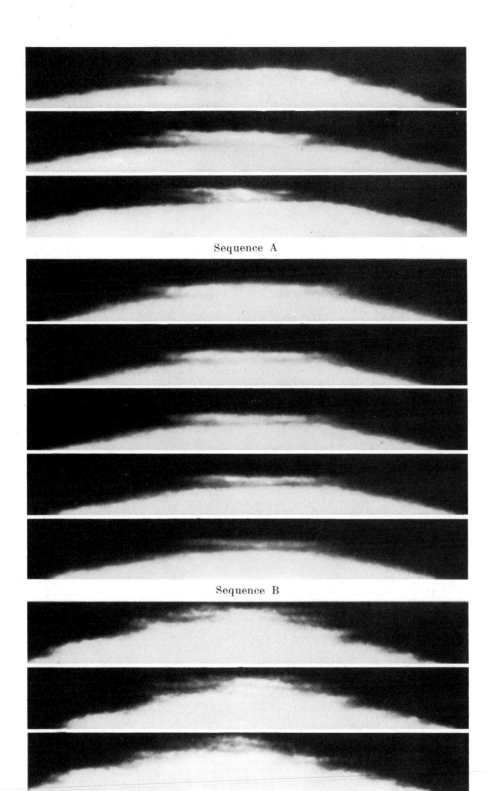

Sequence A

Sequence B

Sequence C

Colour photographs of artificial sunsets (experiment on page 159). ➡

The left hand series (1-4) shows what happens when the lower part of the sun's disc moves gradually downwards into layers of discontinuity. Note the red flash in fig. 1. There is also a red rim. Note the upper rim with blue-bordered notches which contract into detached and vanishing strips, pure blue in colour, as if suspended in space (fig. A-B-C). In all these photographs there is of course no trace of scintillation (or other atmospheric effects). They were taken on Ektachrome B with Zeiss-Tessar. Compare these pictures with those of actual sunsets (p. 119, 129, 143). Fig. M is the ordinary ceiling lamp photographed as in the experiment described on page 159, but without the glass panes M (and less enlarged).

PLATE XXII   165

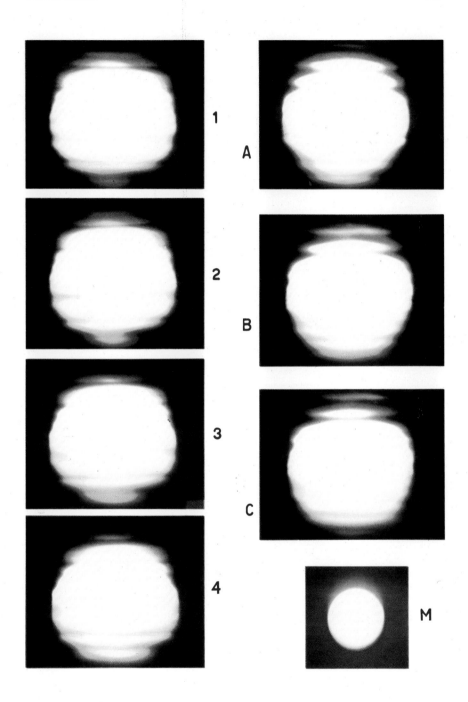

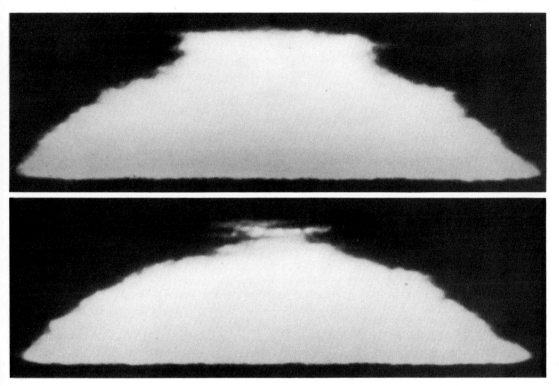

The above photos were taken a few seconds apart. The detached strip shows scintillation effects very near the sea horizon h. The 80 km distant horizon is so sharp (and without scintillation) that individual waves can be distinguished in front of the sun's disc. Compare this horizon with the very disturbed green flash of the same sunset, reproduced in colour on p. 75.

Sunset Sept. 19, 1955. Distant seeing conditions were good. There was a quite different type of scintillation on the sun's upper rim about 10′ above the sea horizon, a mixture of emerald green, yellow and reddish (!) points. The effect was similar to what is seen when moving points of sunlight, reflected from very distant sea-waves, pass through an objective prism in front of the lens and are observed on a ground-glass screen. (Taken on Ektachrome with the 6 m refractor. Sun's diameter 70 cm).

Scintillation Effect on the Rim of the Low Sun, reproduced in colour (highly magnified)

Fig. 1 - Aug. 12, 1954. A detached strip vanishing in a steady coarse-grained mixture of yellow and blue-green light. This type of scintillation (if indeed one should term it such) is denoted in the table on p. 99 with the symbol t. The 80 km distant sea horizon was sharp and without scintillation. See the corresponding black-and-white photographs on p. 167.

Fig. 2 and 3 - Sept. 17, 1954. A flash disappearing with very little scintillation. In figure 3 the flash appears in two layers, whereas it was seen visually in the telescope as triple. The third layer (nearest to the sun's rim) was fainter and is lost in the reproduction. The interval between the two pictures is about 15 seconds. Note the deep notches, with green corners, which precede the flash. This type of observation is denoted by m' in the table on p. 35.

Fig. 4 - Nov. 13, 1954. Distribution of blue and green light within a flash on the very sharp 80 km distant sea horizon (itself without scintillation). Note the blue bridge from the horizon h to the upper strip, which is still yellow with emerald green spikes. The picture belongs to the sunset sequence described on p. 175. Some fine details are lost in the reproduction, which however represents essentially the visual observation.

Fig. 5 - May 31, 1955. This is the only one of the colour photographs of the upper rim of the setting sun that shows a detached strip with a red lower border. Close by were fine spikes with similar colours (lost in the reproduction). Taken about 1º above the horizon with the 6 metre refractor on Ektachrome.

Plate XXIII   169

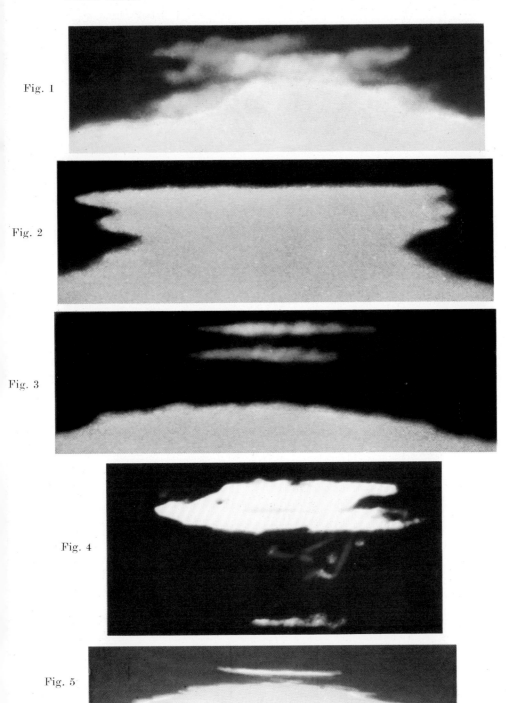

Fig. 1

Fig. 2

Fig. 3

Fig. 4

Fig. 5

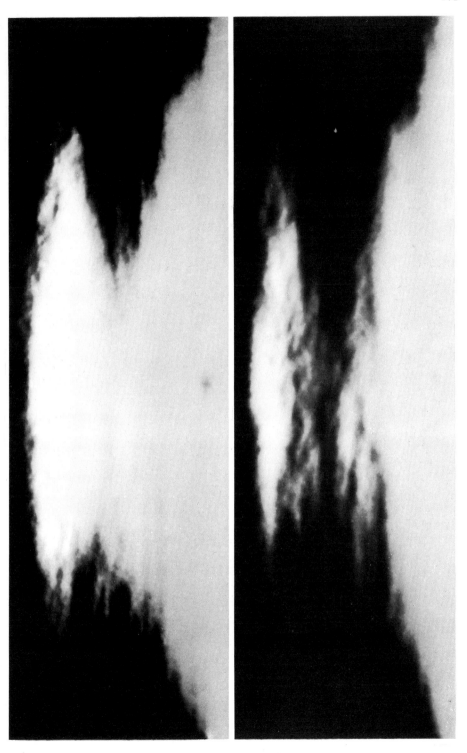

Apr. 10, 1956. Effects of scintillation within a green flash. The detached strip (lower fig.) near the very sharp 80 km distant sea horizon was a pure emerald green, suspended in space for about 4 sec. It was brighter than the portion of the sun's rim just below. Taken with 6 metre refractor. Sun's diameter 35 cm. Notes sunspot in upper photo.

Colour Effects Caused by Incorrect Exposure

It happens not infrequently in photographs of the green and the red flash, and of the green rim with scintillation, that some of the colours are not reproduced exactly as they appear visually in the telescope (correct processing being always presupposed). One chief cause of this is often the existence of horizontal bands of different brightness on the sun's disc (due to haze or to layers of discontinuity), the effect becoming more marked as the sun nears the horizon. Some of these colour effects caused by incorrect exposure have already been discussed (pp. 27-29). A few examples illustrating this point are shown on the following page. These photographs were taken in 1954 with a 4-prism spectrograph of high dispersion. An iron arc was used with a 20 μ slit, Ektachrome Daylight and Ektachrome B. Some of these photographs show clearly what happens with incorrect exposures of the green flash, or of the green and the blue rim of the sun.

On the dark green continuum (fig. B, spectrum g) are seen correctly exposed green lines of the iron arc (all marked '2'). The yellow lines (marked '1') appeared visually as green, but they are more or less over-exposed. This effect shows itself in a colour shift to yellow (more or less), as can be seen clearly in the plate. Compare note (a) on p. 28.

On the dark-blue continuum (fig. A, spectrum f) are seen correctly exposed blue lines (marked 3). The white lines (marked 4) also appear visually a more or less intense blue, but they are over-exposed and consequently more or less white. Compare the relevant note (a) on p. 28.

Strong scintillation on the green rim of the sun can interfere with the exact rendering of the colours on the film, which does not show all the details that can be observed visually (cf note (b) on p. 28). The momentary flare up of a green spike at a point where the dominant colour previously was red or yellow can cause light of different colours to fall successively on a particular spot on the film, if the exposures are not short enough. This effect was imitated in the laboratory in the following manner. The green spectrum g (fig. B) was partially superimposed on a previous exposure of the red iron spectrum r. The resultant is shown in spectrum d, which is thus a mixture of the green and red portions of the iron spectrum on colour film. The dark green lines of g are brighter in d, the yellow lines paler (visually they were an intense green), the red continuum practically disappeared. By varying the exposure times one can obtain other interesting effects.

In figure C a very intense blue line (5) of the iron spectrum was exposed over a double emission line in the solar spectrum (s). It is completely white, except that on the outer edge, on a black background, it has a blue border.

Plate XXIV   173

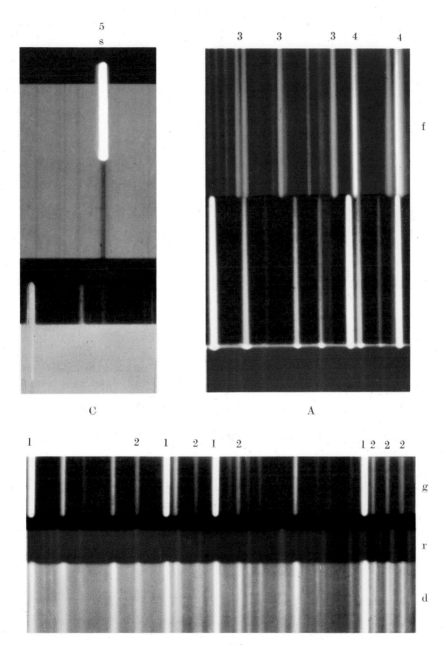

C

A

B

Green and Red Flashes at Sunset, Nov. 13, 1954

This plate shows one of the most difficult flashes to photograph in colour that have been observed in the past three years. The trouble was due to the unusually rapid fading of the light in the yellow disc of the sun (already in contact with the horizon), so that only with difficulty could the exposures be reproduced properly in colour. By taking a mean exposure time, as has usually been done in such cases, it was possible to make black-and-white prints of these Kodachromes. Note in fig. 1 the layered red flash (under-exposed in the original). Its lower edge is almost touching the horizon (not visible in the reproduction). The upper rim of the sun is over-exposed and the green rim is lost by irradiation. The green flash appears at the same height above the horizon as the red flash and is of approximately the same size (fig. 3).

Whatever exposure had been used for this remarkable green flash would probably have been more or less incorrect. While its upper portion (still an intense yellow) hung over the horizon (fig. 3), as if suspended in space, there was suddenly formed (at the moment of the exposure) a faint blue bridge to the horizon h, scintillating points forming a kind of chain and much less bright than the yellow above. "Less bright" is to be understood in a relative sense, for this blue must have appeared very brilliant to the naked eye, since it stands out on the Kodachrome against the almost black (in reality very bright) sky background. As this blue disappeared, the upper yellow portion of the flash changed, from the outer edge inwards, to emerald green, and this remained as the last light or "flash". To the naked eye the whole process must have appeared different. The blue would probably not be seen at all close to the yellow. Perhaps the mixture of blue and yellow may have appeared as green, although no green was really present at this moment. The unaided eye would then receive the impression of a green flash, with a bright tip shooting out of the horizon and somewhat above the horizon, in other words what might be called a "green ray". (Taken with the reflector, f.1. 2.4 m. All the pictures are reproduced with the same magnification).

These difficulties should be borne in mind when viewing the colour reproduction of this flash on page 169 (fig. 4).

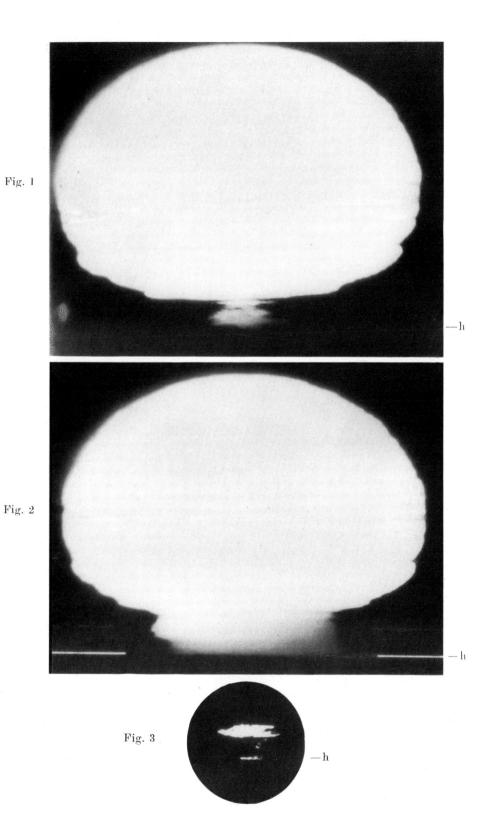

Fig. 1

Fig. 2

Fig. 3

—h

—h

—h

Radiosonde soundings Aug. 13, 1954

Local (Roma-Ciampino)						400 Km distant (Cagliari-Elmas)				
mb	m	°C	wind dir.	wind vel.		mb	m	°C	wind dir.	wind vel.
1002	104	17,0	00°	00		1000	122	22,2	120°	06
1000	121	17,7	00	00		923	800	21,6	130	10
975	330	18,8	00	00		850	1520	17,4	160	04
947	600	17,0	10	10	17	700	3163	9,4	250	10
908	940	16,0	330	14	hours	500	5874	— 6,0	290	19
850	1501	12,6	320	14	before					
818	1850	11,3	310	09	sunset					
798	2050	11,0	290	07						
768	2360	11,0	280	07						
700	3120	7,2	310	09						
635	3900	1,1	310	08						
606	4250	+ 0,1	330	09						
560	4900	— 0,9	310	14						
500	5776	— 9,5	290	25						
1002	104	31,2	270	10		1000	112	24,6	170	18
1000	122	30,5	270	10		960	840	23,5	150	27
850	1539	16,1	30	04		912	900	21,9	120	20
815	1900	12,6	80	02	5	850	1510	21,7	290	17
794	2100	16,6	130	02	hours	700	3173	10,3	240	15
700	3172	9,8	310	05	before	617	4230	3,1	260	16
660	3670	6,5	270	12	sunset	608	4330	3,5	270	16
620	4190	5,5	240	15		500	5890	— 5,4	250	23
562	4960	— 0,8	240	19						
528	5470	-- 1,2	240	23						
500	5879	— 4,9	230	23						
1001	104	19,8	100	07		1000	94	23,2	170	15
1000	113	23,6	100	07		937	680	25,0	140	20
955	500	23,6	100	04	9	887	1120	25,4	150	19
890	1170	19,4	160	13	hours	866	1340	24,2	180	09
850	1520	18,5	180	14	after	850	1500	25,0	210	07
820	1880	17,2	180	13	sunset	700	3159	12,3	290	26
765	2420	13,3	190	10		500	5845	—11,2	290	41
700	3150	7,6	210	12						
500	5850	— 6,8	240	25						

ARROW SHOWS DIRECTION OF SUNSET

12 hours before sunset

12 hours after sunset

Radiosonde soundings Dec. 28, 1955

Local (Roma-Ciampino) — 15 hours before sunset / 400 Km distant (Cagliari-Elmas)

mb	m	°C	wind dir.	wind vel.		mb	m	°C	wind dir.	wind vel.
1007	104	4,2	60°	12		1000	175	8,9	320°	18
1000	161	5,9	50	13		964	410	8,5	330	28
970	431	8,7	30	16		908	980	5,0	340	27
957	530	7,9	30	16	15	890	1130	6,5	340	24
918	870	5,6	40	18	hours	878	1250	5,0	350	21
850	1487	+ 1,0	50	26	before	850	1514	6,7	10	20
813	1860	— 0,8	40	27	sunset	802	1985	+ 0,8	10	27
739	2600	— 7,1	20	33		780	2190	+ 0,5	10	29
700	3014	— 8,8	20	40		725	2700	— 3,9	10	16
667	3388	—11,5	30	49		700	3072	— 4,7	10	35
644	3650	—13,0	30	55		645	3680	8,2	10	27
607	4100	—14,5	30	62		593	4400	13,0	350	40
575	4500	—18,1	30	65		560	4800	15,2	350	40
536	5030	—20,4	20	68		525	5300	16,6	360	44
500	5543	—23,3	20	62		500	5656	19,4	360	60

mb	m	°C	wind dir.	wind vel.		mb	m	°C	wind dir.	wind vel.
1009	104	11,8	50	07		1000	178	13,3	330	09
1000	179	10,9	360	09		920	850	10,7	310	08
850	1113	2,6	360	23		850	1529	5,6	270	09
808	1930	— 0,4	360	24		810	1920	+ 2,2	320	19
786	2150	— 0,6	360	23	3	800	2021	+ 3,0	330	19
767	2340	— 2,0	360	24	hours	700	3085	— 0,6	10	26
749	2540	— 1,8	360	25	before	500	5683	—16,7	10	43
700	3061	— 4,9	20	27	sunset					
665	3470	— 7,4	30	29						
630	3900	— 8,9	30	35						
611	4100	— 9,2	30	37						
544	5000	—14,0	30	46						
500	5640	—18,5	20	52						

mb	m	°C	wind dir.	wind vel.		mb	m	°C	wind dir.	wind vel.
1008	104	4,6	80	08		1000	176	10,2	330	16
1000	169	7,2	60	08		993	190	10,5	330	16
983	330	8,8	10	08		897	1050	4,8	330	30
940	700	6,8	340	09		890	1100	8,2	330	30
850	1503	5,2	350	17	9	850	1516	7,6	350	22
828	1720	7,0	350	15	hours	792	2080	4,0	360	20
712	2950	— 4,0	360	17	after	757	2400	3,3	350	23
680	3300	— 6,5	10	16	sunset	700	3088	— 1,6	350	27
650	3650	— 7,5	20	13		670	3400	— 2,1	350	27
550	4920	—17,6	360	25		600	4303	+ 7,4	340	26
528	5220	—18,1	350	31		527	5260	16,1	350	33
500	5633	—20,2	350	37		500	5692	16,6	340	18

See weather maps on p. 116

Radiosonde soundings Sept. 15, 1956

Local (Roma-Ciampino)

mb	m	°C	wind dir.	wind vel.
1007	104	15,6	120°	07
1000	164	17,7	160	05
968	440	16,9	320	04
886	1170	10,5	210	05
872	1330	10,8	180	06
850	1530	9,4	140	03
832	1720	9,4	110	04
805	1970	8,2	80	08
763	2430	4,8	70	11
710	3000	5,3	40	17
700	3120	3,8	30	18
612	4190	— 4,0	40	23
518	5490	—10,5	30	25
510	5640	—10,0	30	24
500	5770	—10,9	30	24

02h M.E.T.

400 Km distant (Cagliari-Elmas)

mb	m	°C	wind dir.	wind vel.
1000	134	25,6	10°	14
900	1043	16,5	70	12
855	1470	16,0	60	07
850	1529	17,0	60	07
838	1650	15,0	50	06
800	2039	13,0	20	06
700	3146	4,7	40	10
687	3300	3,9	40	11
650	3730	2,5	20	13
583	4600	— 1,9	20	21
500	5821	— 8,9	20	16

Local (Roma-Ciampino) — 14h M.E.T

mb	m	°C	wind dir.	wind vel.
1009	104	27,0	20	05
1000	183	26,4	260	04
892	1170	17,2	20	08
850	1582	16,3	50	11
808	2000	14,0	100	11
765	2470	14,0	70	11
700	3210	8,3	90	12
630	4060	2,1	60	19
617	4240	2,1	60	20
593	4570	— 0,1	70	18
578	4770	— 0,1	70	17
540	5300	— 2,6	50	13
500	5909	— 7,1	20	06

400 Km distant (Cagliari-Elmas) — 14h M.E.T

mb	m	°C	wind dir.	wind vel.
1000	181	27,0	170	16
850	1584	16,1	60	14
806	2000	12,2	70	13
752	2580	11,4	80	12
700	3166	8,8	100	14
619	4170	2,6	110	13
547	5180	— 0,9	80	13
500	5871	— 5,5	360	08

Radiosonde soundings Sept. 16, 1956

Local (Roma-Ciampino) — 02h M.E.T.

mb	m	°C	wind dir.	wind vel.
1011	104	15,2	00	00
1000	198	18,0	00	00
960	540	18,2	260	06
899	1110	14,8	350	03
850	1579	14,2	350	06
826	1810	13,8	40	09
700	3192	5,5	50	08
500	5849	—12,2	110	06

400 Km distant (Cagliari-Elmas) — 02h M.E.T.

mb	m	°C	wind dir.	wind vel.
1005	140	21,1	00	00
1000	197	21,1	00	00
885	1240	15,9	110	16
850	1584	13,5	100	15
772	2370	11,2	130	12
700	3200	7,5	130	14
620	4200	4,7	120	14
500	5892	— 6,9	150	18

Local (Roma-Ciampino) — 14h M.E.T.

mb	m	°C	wind dir.	wind vel.
1009	104	26,6	270	08
1000	183	26,4	270	08
900	1096	16,5	150	02
874	1350	14,0	110	06
868	1400	16,5	100	06
850	1580	16,5	110	04
815	1940	15,6	50	02
700	3210	8,0	100	02
567	4900	— 4,2	220	03
500	5886	— 9,9	210	10

400 Km distant (Cagliari-Elmas) — 14h M.E.T.

mb	m	°C	wind dir.	wind vel.
1000	179	21,1	170	14
953	600	17,3	130	15
925	850	16,5	130	16
893	1150	14,9	130	13
850	1564	14,4	130	12
835	1700	14,4	140	11
787	2200	11,5	150	07
770	2400	11,4	160	09
700	3180	5,7	160	11
660	3650	1,0	150	13
635	3950	1,0	150	16
583	4650	— 2,3	150	23
560	4955	— 4,4	150	22
500	5848	—10,2	150	18

Radiosonde soundings Sept. 17, 1956

Local (Roma-Ciampino) — 400 Km distant (Cagliari-Elmas)

02ʰ M.E.T.

mb	m	°C	wind dir.	wind vel.		mb	m	°C	wind dir.	wind vel.
1007	104	16,0	140°	05		1009	80	20,9	80°	05
1000	164	16,7	130	05		1000	153	20,8	100	05
980	320	16,0	350	03		863	1380	11,6	170	08
970	410	17,0	330	02		850	1531	12,8	170	08
950	600	17,0	290	02		825	1770	11,9	160	09
850	1547	10,8	150	03		785	2200	10,7	160	09
815	1900	10,8	130	04		773	2310	10,7	160	10
732	2790	7,5	110	05		700	3143	3,7	160	10
700	3156	5,2	110	06		665	3560	0,7	170	11
663	3600	2,6	30	04		592	4480	— 3,8	160	19
500	5811	—13,2	240	09		550	5040	— 5,8	170	18
						540	5200	— 7,1	180	17
						500	5796	—12,1	190	19

14ʰ M.E.T.

mb	m	°C	wind dir.	wind vel.		mb	m	°C	wind dir.	wind vel.
1003	104	26,6	290	07		1000	123	21,0	170	12
1000	130	26,5	290	06		960	460	18,8	150	16
880	1210	16,0	240	04		850	1504	10,6	100	09
850	1529	13,6	230	03		805	1960	7,6	130	05
760	2500	8,0	160	05		790	2120	8,2	130	05
745	2630	6,2	150	06		770	2320	8,2	130	05
700	3134	4,6	170	05		720	2870	6,8	170	06
655	3670	1,5	210	10		700	3102	3,8	180	05
500	5781	—14,8	240	10		665	3510	0,7	220	05
						652	3650	0,7	220	06
						620	4070	— 2,5	200	10
						598	4380	— 4,7	200	11
						552	4980	— 7,1	200	08
						527	5350	— 7,5	220	10
						500	5755	—12,5	120	11

Radiosonde soundings Sept. 18, 1956

02ʰ M.E.T.

mb	m	°C	wind dir.	wind vel.		mb	m	°C	wind dir.	wind vel.
1003	104	16,4	150	06		1000	118	19,4	170	06
1000	129	14,0	150	06		850	1493	10,1	210	05
937	690	13,2	40	05		841	1550	9,5	210	05
870	1290	9,6	110	04		815	1820	9,1	270	05
850	1490	8,8	140	06		758	2340	4,7	250	04
825	1740	9,0	160	07		745	2560	4,4	180	03
806	1930	7,0	150	07		735	2670	4,4	180	02
785	2140	5,2	130	07		725	2780	4,1	180	02
769	2300	5,2	120	03		700	3084	1,2	180	04
730	2740	2,0	100	03		590	4440	— 5,2	230	07
700	3075	1,4	120	07		532	5220	—10,7	230	06
648	3670	— 3,7	120	07		500	5717	—14,8	270	07
633	3870	— 4,2	150	06						
582	4540	—10,0	190	05						
500	5682	—18,7	210	08						

14ʰ M.E.T.

mb	m	°C	wind dir.	wind vel.		mb	m	°C	wind dir.	wind vel.
1003	104	27,4	240	11		1000	120	22,4	160	12
1000	130	26,7	240	11		850	1504	12,5	60	06
865	1360	15,4	160	12		735	2200	4,3	340	04
850	1533	15,4	140	14		700	3111	2,7	240	06
812	1930	14,0	130	13		613	4150	— 4,4	280	05
700	3155	5,5	170	05		555	4900	— 5,3	140	05
565	4850	— 6,1	100	04		545	5060	— 7,5	160	07
500	5810	—14,0	140	03		500	5753	—12,5	130	05

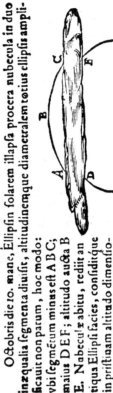

4. Tota Ellipsis frequentes induit, modo supra, modo infra gibbos, ita vt planè irregularis appareret: ꝗ etiam alias frequens est.

5. Tota altitudo Solis inconstanter, non æquabiliter variata fuit. Nam contractior apparens, paulo post altior euasit, vti apparet in Diametro D E ad tabulam obseruationis, quæ cum Sol humilior esset, extitit procerior, cum tamen eidem Sol altior exhibuisset diametrum DF breuiorem, contra ordinarium Refractionis tenorem. Et hoc etiam sæpe alias euenit. Adiectum diagramma oculis subiicit pleraque, AB, Longitudo Solis eadem toto die & obseruationis tempore. CD, & EF, arcus solares in rectam porrecti. CGD, HE, EIF & FK, gibbi solares. Cætera de asperitate alias passim & præsertim in Apelle à nobis sunt dicta: Consule etiam Disquitiones.

Octobris die 10. manè, Ellipsin solarem illapsa procera nubecula in duo inæqualia segmenta diuisit, altitudinemque diametralem totius ellipsis amplificauit non parum, hoc modo: vbi segmentum minus est ABC, maius DEF; altitudo aucta B E. Nabeculæ abitu, rediit antiqua Ellipsis facies, confiditque in pristinam altitudo dimensionem. Tales metamorphoses sæpe alias, etiam in vespertino Solis descensu, notaui. Genuina, inter alias multas, (de quibus suo loco & tempore,) huius apparentiæ ratio videtur esse Refractio à perpendiculari, propterea quod nubecula ACFD densior sit medio inter oculum & ipsam interiecto; è quo fit vt pars Solis ACFD, obscurè tralucens nonnihil amplietur, & sic Ellipseos difformias generetur: id quod in aliis experimentis passim est obuium. Octo-

REFRACTIONES COELESTES,
SIVE
SOLIS ELLIPTICI PHÆNOMENON ILLVSTRATVM;

IN QVO
VARIÆ ATQVE ANTIQVÆ
ASTRONOMORVM CIRCA HANC MAteriam difficultates enodantur, dubia multiplicia dissoluuntur, via ad multa recondita eruenda sternitur:

Opusculum tam Astronomis quàm Physicis perquam vtile, perꝗ necessarium.

AVCTORE

CHRISTOPHORO SCHEINER, SOCIET. IESV PRESBYTERO.

Cum facultate Superiorum.

INGOLSTADII,

Ex Officina Typographica Ederiana, apud Elisabetham Angermariam.
Cum Gratia & Priuilegio Cæsarea Maiestatis.

1 6

Title page of Scheiner's work on the low sun, with specimens of his drawings.

Bibliography

FISHER[34] gives a bibliography of 178 items dealing with the green flash, containing " all the references on the subject in periodical literature that I have found informing ". He searched the literature and gave a list of the periodicals that were available to him. He was a very careful worker and it is unlikely that he missed anything of importance in these journals. In a later paper[35] FISHER mentioned that he was preparing a continuation of his bibliography, but I have not been able to find any later publication by him on this subject (he died in 1934). MULDER,[94] whose book I have not seen, also gives a bibliography. KUIPER's thesis[75] gives all the references in FISHER and MULDER and some additional ones, making over 200 in all. In the present bibliography I have omitted the references contained in the lists of FISHER and KUIPER, except those that I have had occasion to cite in this work. I have also omitted several other items that did not appear to be of sufficient interest to be included, such as mere mention of observations of the green flash without any helpful details. Altogether I have excluded about 200 of the references in my original list. It is of course possible that there are articles on this subject in literature that is not available to me, but I hope that at least no important paper that has appeared in astronomical periodicals has been omitted.

It is often a great help to know the actual title of a paper, and its length, and these are given in the first section of the bibliography. On the other hand, a large proportion of the references are to observations, with much the same title in every case. These have all been grouped in the second section under the general heading " Observations ", without separate titles, both in order to save space and to avoid wearying the reader. There follows a short section containing references to colour photography technique.

The abbreviations are those used in the *Astronomischer Jahresbericht*, Bd. 54.

1. ABBATE Pacha, Bull. de l'Inst. Égyptien (3) 4, 326-327, 1893.
2. H. ARCTOWSKI, *Notice sur les déformations apparentes des astres à l'horizon, observées à bord de la « Belgica »*. Bull. Soc. Belge d'astr. 7, 72-87, 1902.
3. — (the same). Mem. Soc. Spett. 31, 191-197, 1902.
4. Sir G. B. AIRY, *Note on Atmospheric Chromatic Dispersion as Affecting Telescopic Observations and on the Mode of Correcting it.* MNRAS 29, 333-337, 1869; 30, 57-59, 1870.
5. R. G. AITKEN, *The Green Flash.* ASP Leaflet 123 = 3, 177-182, 1939.
6. BAER, *Merkwürdige Refraktionserscheinungen.* Met. Z. 1905, 128-129.
7. E. W. BARLOW, *The Green Flash at Sunrise and Sunset.* Marine Observer, Apr. 1936.

8. D. M. BARRINGER, *Note on the « Green Flash ».* Pop. Astr. **57**, 252-253, 1949.

9. R. BOSCOVICH, *De Litteraria Expeditione* ... Rome 1755, pp. 94-96.

10. C. M. BOTLEY, *L'aria e i suoi misteri,* pp. 245-252, Milano, 1942.

11. Sir D. BREWSTER, *Observations on the lines of the solar spectrum, and on those produced by the Earth's atmosphere.* R. Soc. Edin. Trans. **12**, 519-530, 1834.

12. A. CARPENTER, *The Green Flash at Sunrise and Sunset.* JBAA **22**, 372-378, 1912.

13. — *The Green Flash and the Green Sun.* JBAA **23**, 97-98, 1912.

14. J. J. TAUDIN CHABOT, *Sonnenuntergang und Sonnenaufgang.* Weltall **3**, 266-272, 1903.

15. S. CHANDRASEKHAR, *A statistical basis for the theory of stellar scintillation.* MNRAS **112**, 475-483, 1952.

16. J. F. CHAPPEL, *Apparent Distortions of the Setting Sun.* PASP **45**, 281-282, 1933.

17. A. L. COLTON, *Sunsets at Mount Hamilton, Some Curious Effects of Refraction.* Lick Cont. 5, 71-80, 1895.

18. — *Photographs of the Setting Sun.* PASP **7**, 285, 1895.

19. — Himmel u. Erde, Feb. 1895.

20. L. J. COMRIE, *The Green (?) Flash (?).* JBAA **58**, 280, 1948; Pop. Ast. **57**, 42-43, 1949.

21. G. COUTINHO, *The Artificial Green Flash.* Obs. **42**, 80-82, 1919.

22. H. H. DAHLERUP-PETERSEN, *Det grönne Glint.* NAT **12**, 63, 1931.

23. A. DANJON et G. ROUGIER, *Le spectre et la théorie du rayon vert.* CR **171**, 814-817, 1920.

24. — *Le rayon vert.* BSAF **34**, 513-518, 1920.

25. — *Le rayon vert, étude spectroscopique et théorie.* Strasbourg Ann. 1, 105-115, 1926.

26. C. R. DAVIDSON and F. J. M. STRATTON, *The Green Flash.* Obs **49**, 308, 1926.

27. J. DEVAUX, *Sur le « rayon vert ».* BSAF **42**, 384-389, 1928.

28. N. DIJKWEL, *Enige waarnemingen van de groene straal.* Hemel en Damp. **34**, 235, 258, 1936.

29. J. DUFAY, *Notes sur l'absorption sélective dans l'atmosphère terrestre.* Ann d'Astrophys 5, 93-113, 1942.

30. N. EGOROFF, *Recherches sur le spectre d'absorption de l'atmosphère terrestre à l'Observatoire de Paris.* CR **93**, 788-790, 1881.

31. J. EVERSHED, *The Green Flash.* Nature **95**, 286, 1915.

32. — *The Green Flash at Sunset.* Nature **111**, 13, 1923.

33. — *The Green Flash.* Obs **49**, 369-370, 1926.

34. W. J. FISHER, *Low Sun Phenomena. IV The « Green Flash ».* Pop. Ast. **29**, 251-265, 382-392, 1922.

35. — *The Green Flash — Note on its History and Literature.* PASP **36**, 325-326, 1924.

36. F. A. FOREL, *Les variations de l'horizon apparent.* CR **129**, 272-274, 1899.

37. C. GALLISOT et E. BELLEMIN, *L'observation des accidents optiques de l'atmosphère. L'altitude des stries, signe précurseur du temps.* J. de Physique, 8, 1927.

38. E. GAVIOLA, *On seeing, fine structure of stellar images and inversion layer spectra.* AJ 54, 155-161, 1949.

39. L. GOLDBERG, *The Absorption Spectrum of the Atmosphere,* in G. P. KUIPER, *The Earth as a Planet,* Chicago 1954, pp. 434-490.

40. W. GROFF, *La plus ancienne observation d'un phénomène naturel ou astronomique.* Bull. de l'Inst. Égyptien (3) 4, 149-156, 1893.

41. — *Note sur la plus ancienne observation ...* Bull. de l'Inst. Égyptien (3) 4, 360-364, 1893.

42. H. O. GRONSTRAND, *Den gröna stralen.* PAT 30, 26-36, 1949.

43. F. GUDZENT, *Die Farbenphotographie in der meteorologischen Optik.* Die Himmelswelt 52, 92, 1942.

44. G. GUGLIELMO, *Intorno ad alcune particolarità del « raggio verde ».* R. Accad. dei Lincei Rendic. (5) 25, 296-302, 1916.

45. — *Sulla durata teorica del raggio verde.* R. Accad. dei Lincei Rendic. (5) 25, 417-423, 1916.

46. Ch. E. GUILLAUME, *Le rayon vert.* BSAF 38, 514-515, 1919.

47. W. C. HAINES, *The Green Flash observed October 16, 1929, at Little America by Members of the Byrd Antarctic Expedition.* Monthly Weather Rev. 59, 117-118, 1931.

48. M. HANZAWA, *Green flash observed in the Antarctic Ocean.* Oceanographical Magazine, Tokyo, 1951, 139.

49. E. HAVINGA, *Groene straal en kimduiking.* Hemel en Damp. 32, 114, 1934.

50. P. HENRY, *Sur une méthode de mesure de la dispersione atmosphérique.* CR 112, 377-380, 1891.

51. E. H. HILLS, *Note on the « Green Flash » at Sunset.* MNRAS 62, 431-432, 1902.

52. J. HOPPE, *Das Geheimnis des grünen Sonnenstrahls.* Weltall 34, 43-44, 1934.

53. W. J. HUMPHREYS, *Optics of the Air: Green Flash.* J. Franklin Inst. 188, 452-453, 1919.

54. — *Optics of the Air.* Phys. Rev. (2) 46, 455-462, 1919.

55. — *Note on the Green Ray.* PASP 37, 20, 1925.

56. T. S. JACOBSEN, *On the Spectrum of the Green Flash at Sunset.* JRAS Canada 46, 93-102, 1952 (= Cont. D. A. Obs. Victoria 26).

57. — *The Green Flash at Sunset and at Sunrise.* Sky and Tel. 12, 233-236, 1953.

58. J. JANSSEN, *Sur les raies telluriques du spectre solaire.* CR 56, 538-540, 1863.

59. — *Analyse spectrale des éléments de l'atmosphère terrestre.* CR 101, 649-651, 1885.

60. — *Note sur la loi d'absorption des bandes du spectre de l'oxygène.* CR 121, 1306-1310, 1895.

61. — *Etudes spectrales sur l'oxygène.* Meudon Ann. 2, 9-33, 1906.

62. Chr. JENSEN, *Neues über den « Grünen Strahl ».* Himmelswelt 45, 209-210, 1935.

63. J. P. JOULE, Letter to Manchester Lit. and Phil. Soc., 1869 (quoted in ref. 160).

64. W. H. JULIUS, *Le rayon vert.* Arch. néérl. des sc. (2) **6**, 385-389, 1901.

65. — *Le rayon vert.* Ciel et Terre, **23**, 209-214, 1902.

66. D. KEILIN and F. E. HARTREE, *Observations on the Absorption Spectrum of Oxygen.* Nature **164**, 257-259, 1949.

67. — *Absorption Spectrum of Oxygen.* Nature **165**, 543-544, 1950.

68. G. KELLER, *Astronomical « seeing » and its relation to atmospheric turbulence.* AJ **58**, 113-125, 1953.

69. Lord KELVIN, *Blue Ray of Sunrise over Mont Blanc.* Nature **60**, 411, 1899.

70. — *Life* by S. P. Thomson, **2**, 1147. London 1910.

71. G. Mc K. KNIGHT, *The Green Flash a Sign of Biliousness.* English Mech. **73**, 449, 1901.

72. T. KÖHL, *Solens grönne glimt.* NAT **11**, 69-71, 1930.

73. F. KRIFKA, *Refraktionserscheinungen der aufgehenden Sonne.* Met. Z. **8**, 101-102, 1891.

74. H. KRONE, *Der grüne Strahl kurz vor dem Untergang der Sonne.* Eder's Jahrb. f. Photographie **15**, 12-16, 1901.

75. P. F. KUIPER, *De groene Straal.* Helder, 1926.

76. — *The Green Ray.* JBAA **37**, 231-235, 1927.

77. J. LALANDE, *Astronomie 2*, p. 554, 3e ed., Paris 1792.

78. R. LANGE, S. J., *Le rayon vert.* Rev. des Questions Scient. (3) **30**, 402-426, 1921.

79. S. LEE, *On the dispersive power of the atmosphere.* R. Soc. Lon. Phil. Trans. 1815, 375-383.

80. L. LIBERT, *Déformations solaires et rayon vert.* La Nature **30** (2), 332, 1902.

81. Sir O. LODGE, *The Green Flash.* Nature **120**, 807, 1927.

82. — *The Green Flash.* Nature **121**, 58, 1928.

83. H. M., *Le rayon vert.* Ciel et Terre **68**, 220-222, 1952.

84. A. MACADIE, PASP **36**, 323-324, 1924.

85. F. A. MAVROGORDATO, *Le rayon vert se réflète-t-il sur les nuages?* BSAF **13**, 446-447, 1899.

86. O. MEISSNER, *Kleine Bemerkungen zur atmosphärischen Optik.* Wetter **57**, 263-265, 1940.

87. P. L. MERCANTON, *Encore le « Rayon vert ».* La Nature 1926 (1) suppl. 49.

88. R. MEYER, *Die Entstehung optischer Bilder durch Brechung und Spiegelung in der Atmosphäre.* Met. Z. **52**, 405, 1935.

89. — *Der « grüne Strahl ».* Met. Z. **56**, 342-346, 1939.

90. A. MIETHE, *Dämmerungsbeobachtungen.* Prometheus (Berlin) **20**, 737-740, 753-756, 1909.

91. M. MINNAERT, *Light and Colour in the Open Air*, 2nd. edn., Dover Publ., 1954.

92. C. MONTIGNY, *Essai sur des effets de réfraction et de dispersion produits par l'air atmosphérique.* Acad. R. de Belg. Mém. Cour. **26**, n. 4, 1-70, 1855.

93. — *Note sur des phénomènes de coloration des bords du disque solaire près de l'horizon*. Acad. R. de Belg. Bull. **28**, 425-434, 1869.

94. M. E. MULDER, *The Green Ray or Green Flash at Rising and Setting of the Sun*. The Hague 1922.

95. G. MÜLLER u. E. KRON, *Die Extinktion des Lichtes in der Erdatmosphäre und die Energieverteilung im Sonnenspektrum nach spektralphotometrischen Beobachtungen auf der Insel Teneriffa*. Potsdam Publ. 64, 1-92, 1912.

96. F. NANSEN, *Farthest North*, **1**, 360. London 1897.

97. A. A. NIJLAND, Hemel en Damp. **33**, 435-440, 1935.

98. J. OFFORD, *The Green Tints of Sunset*. Nature **75**, 342, 1907.

99. R. T. OMOND, *A Green Light at Sunset*. Nature **35**, 391, 1886.

100. H. K. PAETZOLD, *Ein Beitrag zur atmosphärischen Extinktion*. AN **281**, 17-22, 1952.

101. J. M. PERNTER u. F. M. EXNER, *Meteorologische Optik*. 2. Aufl. Wien u. Leipzig 1922.

102. C. D. PERRINE, *On the Cause of the Green Ray seen at Sunset*. PASP **36**, 319-322, 1924.

103. — *On the Cause of the « Green Flash » seen at Sunset*. PASP **38**, 134-136, 1926.

104. W. M. FLINDERS PETRIE, *The Green Flash*. Nature **94**, 88, 1914.

105. W. H. PICKERING, *Additional Note on the Green Flash*. MNRAS **62**, 85, 1901.

106. J. C. PIOT Bey, CR **127**, 893-894, 1898.

107. J. PLASSMANN, *Ueber die Färbung der tiefstehenden Sonne und einige Nebenerscheinungen*. Met. Z. **48**, 421-425, 1931.

108. A. W. PORTER and E. TALBOT PARIS, *A demonstration of the green flash at the setting of an artificial sun*. Nature **95**, 194, 1915.

109. W. PRINZ, *Photographies du soleil couchant*. Album jubilaire de l'ass. belge de photographie, 1874-78.

110. L. R., *The Green Ray*. Pop. Ast. **58**, 419-420, 1950.

111. E. RAHIR, *Observation sur le rayon vert au coucher du soleil*. Ciel et Terre **51**, 158-160, 1935.

112. Lord RAYLEIGH, *Normal Atmospheric Dispersion as the Cause of the « Green Flash » at Sunset, with Illustrative Experiments*. Proc. Roy. Soc. A **126**, 311-318, 1930.

113. — *Further Experiments in Illustration of the Green Flash at Sunset*. Proc. Phys. Soc. **46**, 487-498, 1934.

114. F. W. REYNOLDS, *The Green Ray*. English Mech. **50**, 77, 1889.

115. A. RICCÒ, *Immagine del sole riflessa nel mare prova della rotondità della terra*. Mem. Soc. Spett. Ital. **17**, 203-220, 1888.

116. — *Green Light at Sunrise and Sunset*. Nature **35**, 584, 1887.

117. — *Deformazione del disco solare all'orizzonte per causa della rifrazione atmosferica*. Mem. Soc. Spett. Ital. **30**, 96-100, 1901.

118. A. R(ICCÒ), *Photographies des déformations du soleil couchant*. Mem. Soc. Spett. Ital. **31**, 36-39, 1902.

119. E. D. ROE, *On the Appearance of Sunset at Sea*. Pop. Ast. **14**, 444-445, 1906.

120. G. Rougier, *À propos du « rayon vert »*. BSAF **42**, 377-384, 1928.
121. Royal Society Report on Krakatoa Eruption of 1883. London 1888.
122. F. Ruda, *Sulla spiegazione del raggio verde*. R. Accad. dei Lincei Rendic. (6) **6**, 152-156, 228-230, 1927.
123. L. Rudaux, *Déformations du soleil à l'horizon*. BSAF **20**, 283-285, 1906.
124. — *Photographie du rayon vert*. La Nature 1925 (2), 303-304.
125. — *Couchers de soleil et rayon vert*. BSAF **40**, 16, 1926.
126. F. Santschi, *Nouvelles notes sur le rayon vert*. La Nature 1926 (2), suppl. 5.
127. C. Scheiner, S. J., *Rosa Ursina sive Sol*. Bracciani, 1626-1630.
128. — *Refractiones coelestes, sive solis elliptici phaenomenon illustratum*. Ingolstadt, 1617 (X + 162 pp.).
129. G. Schröder, *Weiteres vom « Grünen Strahl »*. Ann. d. Hydrog., zweites Köppen-Heft, 91-93, 1936.
130. — *Der grüne Strahl*. Seewart **10**, 182-184, 1941.
131. G. Schröder, W. Hartmann, O. Klaehn, *Vom « Grünen Strahl »*. Ann. d. Hydrog. **65**, 489-496, 1937.
132. Sir A. Schuster, Trans. Internat. Union for Co-op. in Solar Research, **3**, 55, 1911.
133. — *The « Green Ray » or « Green Flash » at Rising and Setting of the Sun* (review of Mulder's book). Nature **110**, 370-371, 1922.
134. W. H. Steavenson, *The Green Fringe*. JBAA **59**, 41, 1948.
135. W. Swan, *Green Sunlight*. Nature **29**, 76, 1883.
136. P. G. Tait, *On mirage*. R. Soc. Edin. Proc. **11**, 354-361, 1882; Trans. **30**, 551-578, 1883.
137. — *State of the atmosphere which produces the form of mirage observed by Vince and by Scoresby*. Nature **28**, 84-88, 1883.
138. A. D. Thackeray, *Setting of Bright Planet or Star*. JBAA **62**, 206-207, 1952.
139. L. Thollon, *Études sur les raies telluriques du spectre solaire*. CR **91**, 520-522, 1880.
140. G. A. Tikhov, *Sur la dispersion anomale de la lumière dans l'atmosphère terrestre*. Poulkovo Circ. 17, 1-12, 1936.
141. E. Touchet, *Sur le « rayon vert »*. La Nature 1925 (1), 358-366.
142. — *La photographie en couleurs du rayon vert*. BSAF **46**, 89-92, 1932.
143. V. Turquan, *Rayon vert et rayon rouge*. BSAF **13**, 444-446, 1899.
144. H. C. van de Hulst, *The atmospheric oxygen bands*. Ann. d'Astroph. 8, 12-25, 1945.
145. J. Verne, *Le Rayon Vert*. Paris 1882.
146. S. W. Visser, *Dutch Observations of the Green Flash*. PASP **42**, 336-339, 1930.
147. — *The Novaya-Zemlya Phenomenon*. Kon. Ned. Akad. v. Wet. Proc. B **59**, 375-385, 1956.
148. S. W. Visser en J. Th. Verstelle, *Groene Straal en Kimduiking*. Hemel en Damp. **32**, 80-87, 1934.
149. A. Wegener, *Elementare Theorie der atmosphärischen Spiegelungen*. Ann. d. Physik (4) **57**, 203-230, 1918.

150. — *Optik der Atmosphäre*, in MÜLLER-POUILLET, Lehrb. d. Physik, **5**, 199-298. Braunschweig 1928.

151. K. WEGENER, *Der grüne Strahl*. Met. Z. **54**, 427-428, 1937.

152. F. J. W. WHIPPLE, *An experiment illustrating the green flash*. Brit. Ass. for the Adv. of Science, Report 1924, p. 359.

153. C. T. WHITMELL, *The Green Ray and the Green Sun*. JBAA **8**, 95-96, 1897.

154. — *The Green Flash and the Green Sun*. JBAA **23**, 98-100, 1912.

155. — *The Red Flash*. Nature **94**, 61, 1914.

156. — *The Green Flash*. Nature **95**, 35-36, 1915.

157. — *A Red Flash and Three Green Flashes*. JBAA **28**, 228, 1918.

158. — *The Green Flash*. Obs **42**, 123-124, 1919.

159. R. WILSON, *The Blue Sun of 1950, September*. MNRAS **111**, 478-489, 1951.

160. D. WINSTANLEY, *Atmospheric refraction and the last rays of the setting sun*. Manchester Lit. and Phil. Soc. Proc. **13**, 1-4, 1873.

161. — Nature **9**, 20, 1873.

162. R. W. WOOD, *Factors which determine the occurrence of the Green Ray*. Nature **121**, 501, 1928.

163. — *Green Ray Seen from Ship*. Pop. Ast. **36**, 382-383, 1928.

Observations

164. A. B. ACIN, BSAF **34**, 530, 1920.

165. R. G. AITKEN, PASP **39**, 323-324, 1927.

166. — PASP **41**, 317, 1929.

167. L. W. ANTONOW, Mitt. Geogr. USSR **86**, n. 1, 102-104, 1954.

168. D. R. BARBER, Nature **156**, 146, 1945.

169. S. BARKER, JBAA **28**, **71**, 1917.

170. S. J. BARNETT, Nature **122**, 171, 1928.

171. — Nature **125**, 446, 1930.

172. — Phys. Review (2) **46**, 75-76, 1934.

173. E. BAUER et A. DANJON, BSAF **40**, 223-224, 1926.

174. R. M. BELL, Nature **135**, 992, 1935.

175. P. BERGSOË, NAT **13**, 51, 1932.

176. J. T. BIRD, JBAA **38**, 305, 1928.

177. P. BLANC, BSAF **46**, 87-88, 1932.

178. G. BLUM, BSAF **45**, 452, 1931.

179. — BSAF **48**, 563, 1934.

180. N. BONEFF, BSAF **50**, 688-589, 1936.

181. O. BOULET, **35**, 17, 1921.

182. J. BOULINIER, BSAF **42**, 529, 1928.

183. J. E. BOWMAN, JBAA **59**, 40, 1948.

184. E. J. BUGOSLAWSKAJA, Bull. Astr. Geod. USSR n. 12, 32-34, 1953.

185. A. BURONNET, BSAF **46**, 88-89, 1932.

186. CAMUSET, BSAF **35**, 404, 1921.

187. A. CARPENTER, JBAA **24**, 216, 1914.

188. — JBAA **34**, 157, 1924.

189. C. J. P. Cave, Obs **49**, 307-308, 1926.
190. — Nature **120**, 876, 1927.
191. J. J. Taudin Chabot, Met. Z. **17**, 426, 1900.
192. — Met. Z. **18**, 181, 1901.
193. E. A. Childe, English Mechanic **80**, 299, 1904.
194. — JBAA **34**, 183-184, 1928.
195. W. Collman, Ann. d. Hydrog. **70**, 326-327, 1942.
196. A. Cornu, BSAF **11**, 427, 1897.
197. P. Crépy, BSAF **38**, 8, 1924.
198. R. Croste, BSAF **46**, 250, 1932.
199. G. Dam, NAT **13**, 15, 1932.
200. C. Davidson and F. J. M. Stratton, Obs **49**, 156-157, 1926.
201. P. Doig (editor), JBAA **59**, 105-106, 1949.
202. W. G. Duffield, Obs **37**, 452-453, 1914.
203. — Nature **95**, 66, 1915.
204. T. S. Dymond, Nature **123**, 207, 1929.
205. W. F. A. Ellison, English Mechanic **81**, 155, 1905.
206. — English Mechanic **82**, 183, 1906.
207. J. Evershed, Nature **120**, 876-877, 1927.
208. G. C. F., BSAF **42**, 256-257, 1928.
209. M. Farman, BSAF **34**, 426, 1920.
210. R. Fingado, Rev. Soc. Astr. Esp. y Amer. **22**, 103, 1932.
211. G. Flaisleu, BSAF **29**, 410, 1915.
212. C. Flammarion, BSAF **28**, 425-426, 1914.
213. H. Fleury, BSAF **42**, 582, 1928.
214. M. Fouché, BSAF **27**, 484, 1913.
215. R. Gindre, BSAF **46**, 177-178, 1932.
216. M. Groubé, BSAF **43**, 252, 1929.
217. H. L. H., English Mechanic **104**, 112, 1917.
218. J. A. Hardcastle, JBAA **15**, 366, 1905.
219. M. B. B. Heath, JBAA **39**, 61 1928.
220. W. B. Housman, JBAA **39**, 31-32, 1928.
221. A. Ignatoff, BSAF **27**, 500, 1913.
222. R. T. A. Innes, PASP **37**, 106, 1925.
223. G. Isely, BSAF **28**, 271, 1914.
224. L. Jacchia, BSAF **43**, 252, 1929.
225. T. Kellen, Kosmos **23**, 13, 1926.
226. C. Kellner, Die Sterne **14**, 211, 1934.
227. T. Köhl, PASP **37**, 173, 1925.
228. K. R. Kupffer, Korrespondenz Blatt Naturf. Ver. Riga, 1937.
229. Legras, BSAF **36**, 518, 1922.
230. W. G. Levander, JBAA **25**, 349, 1915.
231. W. Ley, Pop. Ast. **57**, 147, 1949.
232. F. Link, Riše hvězd **13**, 44-45, 1932.
233. K. J. Lucaj, Weltkunde **15**, 58-59, 1927.
234. J. P. Maclear, Knowledge **3**, 353, 1906.
235. J. Malburet, BSAF **40**, 222-223, 1926.
236. A. Marquet, BSAF **45**, 70-71, 1931.
237. H. de Maubeuge, CR **103**, 1147-1148, 1886.

238. — La Nature, 1887 (1), 46.
239. — La Nature, 1898 (2), 287.
240. — CR **127**, 453, 1898.
241. — Rev. Scient. **10**, 471, 1898.
242. A. S. D. MAUNDER, JBAA **38**, 305, 1928.
243. E. W. MAUNDER, JBAA **23**, 17, 1912.
244. J. W. MEARES, JBAA **28**, 71, 1917.
245. A. MEE, JBAA **8**, 136-137, 1897.
246. — BSAF **12**, 45-46, 1898.
247. G. MENIER, BSAF **46**, 250, 1932.
248. P. L. MERCANTON, BSAF **47**, 73-74, 1933.
249. H. R. MILL, Nature **120**, 876, 1927.
250. F. C. MOLESWORTH, JBAA **54**, 180, 1944.
251. T. MOLYNEUX, JBAA **16**, 31, 1905.
252. H. MONCHARMONT, BSAF **46**, 115, 1932.
253. C. MOSTYN, Nature **44**, 352, 1891.
254. N. A. MOLLER NICOLAISEN, NAT 1953, 117-118.
255. A. A. NIJLAND, Met. Z. **19**, 335, 1902.
256. — Hemel en Damp, **33**, 219, 1935.
257. W. NORLIND, AN **253**, 171-172, 1934.
258. — AN **254**, 216, 1935.
259. — Pop. Ast., **57**, 301, 1949.
260. M. OLMSTED, PASP **37**, 105-106, 1925.
261. M. P., Hemel en Damp. **31**, 448, 1933.
262. J. A. PARKER, JBAA **39**, 222, 1929.
263. I. I. PUTILIN, Russ. Ast. Circ. 118, 9-11, 1951.
264. — Bull. Astron. Geod. USSR **12**, 26-32, 1953.
265. J. RANNEFT, Hemel en Damp. **47**, 159, 1949.
266. Lord RAYLEIGH, Nature **135**, 760, 1935.
267. H. P. REDINGTON, PASP **41**, 388, 1929.
268. C. RENARD, BSAF **40**, 221-222, 1926.
269. J. RIEM, AN **200**, 51-54, 1914.
270. O. F. T. ROBERTS, Nature **126**, 169, 1930.
271. D. ROGUET, BSAF **23**, 21, 1908.
272. L. RUDAUX, La Nature 1904 (2), 294.
273. H. E. RUDDY, BSAF **51**, 128, 1937.
274. F. SANTSCHI, La Nature 1923 (2), 193.
275. A. SAWRUCHIN, Russ. Ast. Circ. 120, 8, 1951.
276. W. W. SCHARANOW, Russ. Ast. Circ. 108, 9-11, 1950.
277. — Priroda **40**, n. 7, 50-53, 1951.
278. G. SCHINDLER, Die Sterne **14**, 136-137, 1934.
279. G. SCHRÖDER, Ann. d. Hydrog. **63**, 336-340, 1935.
280. Sir A. SCHUSTER, Nature **95**, 8, 1915.
281. W. SEMPLE, Nature **120**, 877, 1927.
282. A. SENONQUE, BSAF **15**, 56, 1901.
283. J. L. A. SILLEM, Obs **49**, 246, 1926.
284. R. E. G. SIMMONS, J. Inst. of Navigation, 4, 415, 1951.
285. C. MICHIE SMITH, Nature **41**, 538, 1890.
286. W. W. SPANGENBERG, Met. Z. **56**, 201, 1939.

287. J. STEBBINS, PASP **39**, 323, 1927.

288. R. DE TERWAGNE, Gaz. Astr. **21**, 162, 1934.

289. E. THIBAULT, BSAF **49**, 15, 1935.

290. H. F. TIARKS, JBAA **42**, 226, 1932.

291. « TREADLE », English Mechanic **80**, 183, 340, 1904.

292. W. M. TSCHERNOW, Russ. Ast. Cirs. 120, 8-9, 1951.

293. G. VERHAS, BSAF **16**, 163, 1902.

294. E. B. VIGNOLES, JBAA **42**, 302-303, 1932.

295. R. WHITEHEAD, BSAF **35**, 404, 1921.

296. C. T. WHITMELL, JBAA **12**, 289-290, 1902.

297. — JBAA **22**, 433-434, 1912.

298. — English Mechanic **104**, 30, 1917.

299. — JBAA **29**, 25, 1918.

300. F. P. WORLEY, Nature **135**, 760, 1935.

301. I. YAMAMOTO, Kyoto Bull. **3**, 294, 1934.

302. — Kyoto Bull. **4**, 308, 1935.

303. (Passengers on St. Laurent), BSAF **14**, 236, 1900; Met. Z. **17**, 426, 1900; Naturw. Rundschau **15**, 259, 1900; Rev. Scient. **12**, 406, 1900.

304. Bull. astr. ass. du Nord **14**, 14-16, 1940.

305. JBAA **62**, 90, 1952.

306. Marine Observer **21**, 216, 1951.

307. Nature **135**, 866, 1925.

Colour Photography

308. H. BERGER, *Agfacolor* (Italian edition). Wuppertal 1950.

309. EASTMAN KODAK Co., *Color as Seen and Photographed: Problems in Color Photography*, 1951, p. 50.

310. — *Color Photography in the Studio*, 1954, p. 65.

311. — *Making Duplicates on Miniature Kodachrome Film*. Kodak Photographic Notebook, 1951.

312. — *Photography with Kodachrome*, 1941, p. 48.

313. A. FEININGER, *Successful Color-Photography*. New York 1955.

Subject Index

The index is both to the book and to the bibliography. The numbers preceded by **A** are those of the pages in this work where the subject is discussed or illustrated; the numbers following **B** are those of the references in the bibliography.

Discussion of Green Flash **B** 5, 9, 23, 24, 25, 34, 51, 57, 62, 75, 76, 78, 83, 89, 91, 94, 97, 101, 131, 146, 150, 160, 161, 162.

Green Flash at Sunrise **A** pp. 10, 23, 24-25, 41, 43-51. **B** 5, 7, 12, 14, 27, 34, 40, 44, 57, 69, 104, 116, 120, 135, 140, 143, 148, 179, 187, 189, 192, 202, 203, 207, 215, 217, 218, 223, 227, 234, 237, 238, 239, 240, 241, 251, 253, 255, 260, 274, 280, 282, 291.

Violet Flash **A** p. 23. **B** 27, 34, 70, 120, 126, 141, 193, 248, 260, 299.

Red Flash **A** pp. 23, 101-115, 117, 119, 121, 143, 174-175. **B** 9, 91, 143, 155, 157, 296, 297, 298, 305, 306.

Repetitions of Flash **B** 34, 148, 172, 183, 186, 198, 213, 227, 253, 260, 279.

Duration of Flash **A** pp. 18-19. **B** 25, 34, 45, 47, 50, 57, 75, 76, 91, 104, 140, 158, 183, 186, 198, 213, 227, 295.

Effect of Height of Observer **A** pp. 14-15. **B** 21, 91, 148, 248.

Effect of Atmospheric Humidity **A** p. 15. **B** 23, 24, 75, 76, 191, 285.

Sunspots - Green and Red Rim **A** p. 23. **B** 78, 92, 109, 118, 127.

Green or Red Flash on Rising or Setting of Venus, Jupiter or Bright Star **A** pp. 19, 67, 69. **B** 25, 27, 31, 32, 33, 40, 75, 109, 118, 138, 148, 164, 173, 205, 206, 225, 234, 261, 275, 303, 305, 306.

Green Flash on Moon **B** 40, 279.

Abnormal Refraction **A** pp. 20-21. **B** 9, 10, 17, (p. 78), 34, 36, 47, 54, 75, 76, 77, 101 (pp. 84-109), 140, 146, 147, 150, 187, 208.

Mirage, Inversion Layers, Reflections **A** pp. 19-20, 101-115, 131-141, 143, 151, 152, 153-158. **B** 9, 27, 34, 54, 75, 76, 78, 88, 91 (pp. 43-53), 101 (pp. 109-188), 136, 137, 149, 150.

Effect of Mirage on Green Flash **A** pp. 19-20, 101-115, 131-141. **B** 31, 32, 33, 34, 56, 75, 76, 78, 84, 91, 140, 146, 162, 163, 253.

Vertical Extension of Green Rim **A** pp. 17, 18, 20, 21, 34, 35. **B** 44.

Distortions of Low Sun **A** pp. 17-18, 61, 63, 101-115, 117-129, 131-141, 143, 180. **B** 2, 3, 6, 16, 17, 18, 19, 34, 73, 75, 80, 87, 91 (pp. 53-58), 96, 101 (pp. 155-161), 109, 115, 117, 118, 119, 123, 128, 141, 146, 148, 150 (pp. 220-225), 196, 272.

Selective Absorption in Atmosphere **A** pp. 15-17. **B** 11, 23, 24, 25, 29, 30, 39, 56, 58, 59, 60, 61, 64, 65, 66, 67, 95, 100, 132, 139, 140, 144.

Scintillation, Seeing **A** pp. 3, 21-22, 29, 35, 43, 53, 59, 61, 77, 87-93, 95, 103-115, 116, 143, 161-163, 167-171. **B** 15, 37, 38, 68, 91 (pp. 63-73), 101 (pp. 188-241), 150 (pp. 204-207).

Spectrum of Green Rim and Green Flash **A** pp. 12-17. **B** 23, 24, 25, 28, 44, 56, 140.

Experiments **A** pp. 12-14, 24-25, 153-158, 159-160, 164-165. **B** 21, 44, 108, 112, 113, 122, 140, 152.

Effects of Under- or Over-Exposure on Colour Photographs **A** pp. 26, 27-29, 55, 57, 65, 69, 172-173.

Name Index

Abbott, C. G., 16.
Airy, G. B., 9.
Aitken, R. G., 10, 18, 2
Arctowski, H., 22.

Baer, 22.
Barnard, E. E., 23.
Barringer, D. M., 11.
Baxendell, J., 10.
Bellemin, E., 21.
Bessel, F. W., 9.
Botley, C. M., 8.
Brewster, D., 15.
Byrd, R., 18.

Chandrasekhar, S., 21, 22.
Chappel, J. F., 22.
Claude Lorrain, 9.
Colton, A. L., 22, 100.
Coutinho, G., 14.
Corot, J. B., 9.

Danjon, A., 11, 13.
Devaux, J., 21.
Dufay, J., 15, 16.

Evershed, J., 19.

Fisher, W. J., 10, 29.

Gallisot, C., 21.
Gaviola, E., 21.
Gindre, R., 23.
Goldberg, L., 16.
Groff, W., 7.
Guglielmo, G., 12, 13, 14, 18, 20.

Haines, W. C., 18.
Hanzawa, M., 24.
Hartree, F. E., 15.
Havinga, E., 15.
Helmholtz, H. von, 18.
Hertzsprung, E., 23.

Jacobsen, T. S., 10, 15, 19, 20, 23, 24.
Janssen, J., 15, 16.
Jensen, Chr., 10.
Joule, J. P., 10.
Julius, W. H., 12, 13.

Keilin, D., 15.
Keller, G., 21.
Kelvin, Lord, 10, 11.
Kepler, J., 20.
de Kerolyr, M., 24.
Krifka, F., 22.
Kron, E., 16.
Kuiper, P. F., 10, 15, 29.

Lee, S., 9.
Lodge, O., 11.

Meyer, R., 10.
Minnaert, M., 18.
Mulder, M. E., 10, 29.
Müller, G., 16.

Newton, I., 9.
Nijland, A. A., 10.

Offord, J., 7.

Perrine, C. D., 12.
Petrie, W. M. F., 7.
Piot Bey, 7.
Pickering, W. H., 11.
Porter, A. W., 11.

Rayleigh, Lord, 14, 17, 20, 22, 30.
Riccò, A., 22.
Rougier, G., 11, 13.
Ruda, F., 13, 14.
Rudaux, L., 22.

Scheiner, C., 8, 9, 22, 157, 180.
Schuster, A., 12, 16.
Shackleton, E., 21.
Swan, W., 10, 11.

Tait, P. G., 22.
Tikhov, G. A., 13, 14, 20.
Treusch, C., 7, 19, 24, 26, 30, 32, 34, 99, 100, 103.

Verne, J., 10.
Verstelle, J. Th., 20.
Visser, S. W., 10, 20, 21.

Wegener, A., 20, 21, 22, 23, 61.
Whitmell, C. T., 18.
Winstanley, D., 10.
Wood, R. W., 19, 20.